THE HUMAN CONDITION

This course is dedicated to the memory of Dr Richard Holmes, a Senior Lecturer in Biology (1971–1993) and former Pro-vice-chancellor for Student Affairs at the Open University. Richard's vision was an inspiration in laying the foundations for *Human Biology and Health*.

SK220 Book 4
A second level course

THE HUMAN CONDITION

HUMAN BIOLOGY AND HEALTH

BOOK 4

Edited by Frederick Toates

The SK220 Course Team

Course Team Chair

Michael Stewart

Course Manager

Verena Forster

Course Team Secretary

Dawn Partner

Academic Editors

Brian Goodwin (Book 1)
Michael Stewart (Books 2 and 3)
Jill Saffrey (Book 3)
Frederick Toates (Book 4)
Heather McLannahan (Book 5)

Authors

Janet Bunker (Books 1, 2 and 3)
Melanie Clements (Book 3)
Basiro Davey (Books 1 and 2)
Brian Goodwin (Book 1)
Linda Jones (Book 1)
Jeanne Katz (Book 5)
Heather McLannahan (Book 5)
Hilary MacQueen (Books 1 and 4)
Jill Saffrey (Book 3)
Moyra Sidell (Book 5)
Michael Stewart (Book 2)
Margaret Swithenby (Book 1)
Frederick Toates (Books 2, 3 and 4)

Editors

Andrew Bury
Sheila Dunleavy
Sue Glover
Gillian Riley
Margaret Swithenby

Design Group

Martin Brazier (Designer)
Sarah Hofton (Designer)
Steve Best (Graphic Artist)
Andrew Whitehead (Graphic Artist)

BBC

Sandra Budin
Rissa de la Paz
Phil Gauron
Paul Manners
Ian Thomas
Nick Watson

OU Course Consultant

Chris Inman

External Course Consultant

Bill Tuxworth (University of Birmingham)

External Course Assessor

Professor Jennifer Boore (University of Ulster)

First published 1997. Reprinted 2002

Edited, designed and typeset in the United Kingdom by the Open University.

Printed and bound in Singapore under supervision of MRM Graphics Ltd, Winslow, Bucks.

ISBN 0 7492 81545

This text forms part of an Open University Second Level Course. If you would like a copy of *Studying with The Open University*, please write to the Course Reservations and Sales Centre, PO Box 724, The Open University, Walton Hall, Milton Keynes, MK7 6ZS. If you have not enrolled on the Course and would like to buy this or other Open University material, please write to Open University Educational Enterprises Ltd, 12 Cofferidge Close, Stony Stratford, Milton Keynes, MK11 1BY, United Kingdom.

1.2

CONTENTS

CHAPTER 1
INTRODUCTION

The title of Book 4 – *The Human Condition* – might have caused you to wonder what is so special about this particular book. Surely, you might reason, the whole of a course entitled *Human Biology and Health* is bound to concern the human condition. You would be right to think along such lines, but what is different in this case is that, perhaps more than the earlier books, Book 4 is intended to stimulate your thinking about what is *peculiar* about human biology and behaviour as compared to that of other species.

At the one level of explanation, humans are collections of cells organized in complex ways to form tissues and for some purposes they might best be understood in such terms. Thus much of what you have learned so far is equally applicable to humans and non-humans. For example, insulin promotes glucose transport and action potentials are transmitted along axons in the same way in both rats and humans. Indeed, much of our knowledge of human biology has been gained from looking at other species and by taking a reductionist approach. For example, Video programme 3, *A nervous encounter*, showed how the basic property of the action potential is much the same in squids as in humans. However, SK220 is also about holistic ways of looking at human biology and behaviour. As you are well aware by now, an holistic approach does not consider a human being as simply a collection of cells forming tissues which make up the organs of the various physiological systems described in the earlier books. Rather, we have conscious awareness, a culture and insight into our condition. This means that in order to understand the complexity of human biology we need to consider it within its psychological and sociological context. The topics we have chosen to look at in Book 4 all demonstrate this need to adopt an approach that considers both what we have in common with other species as well as the fascinating peculiarity of humans.

This book is concerned with the human experiences of sexuality, pain, stress and sleep. In each case, we can gain a certain amount of understanding of the basic processes involved, by looking at non-humans. For example, the hormone testosterone which plays a role in the processes underlying rat reproduction is the same substance as that in humans. As far as we know, testosterone has a similar function in sensitizing nervous system processes in all mammalian species, such that the response to sexual stimuli is increased. Although the form that sexual motivation and behaviour take are rather different in humans compared to non-humans, the hormonal systems involved are remarkably similar. Rats copulate in a fairly stereotyped way. By contrast, the infinite variety and flexibility of human sexual behaviour hardly needs mentioning. We are the only species that understands that there is a relationship between sexual behaviour and reproduction. The fact that we understand this makes possible both the technology of contraception and the seeking of advice to maximize fertility chances.

The richness of human diversity is also shown in the situations that stress us. The so-called stress hormone, adrenalin, is the same in all mammalian species. As with sex, what is different is not so much the basic biology as the context within which these biological processes operate.

❑ Given that adrenalin is released from the adrenal glands in both humans and non-humans (e.g. rats), can you suggest some aspects of stress that are common between species and some aspects that are fundamentally different?

■ What is common is the basic physiology of activation of the sympathetic nervous system and the release of adrenalin from the adrenal glands in response to the threat of danger. What is rather different is the nature of the stimuli that trigger this reaction. For example, as far as we know, we are the only species able to stress ourselves by projecting our imagination far into the future and creating frightening scenarios therein.

Similarly, the basic process for detecting tissue damage by means of nociceptive neurons is much the same in all mammalian species. However, humans are the only species able to understand and think about the significance of such signals. We have a brain and a culture that enables us to 'worry ourselves to death' in response to slight aches and pain.

Putting humans in a special place is not intended to deny the worth of other animals. Of course, from ethical considerations non-humans need to be treated with respect. For example, a rabbit is not simply a warm and furry version of a clockwork toy. Neither should we underestimate the intelligence of other animal species. However, it is surely right to suggest that certain features, such as the possession of a sophisticated level of conscious awareness, might well be peculiar to humans. Of relevance to experimenters is the fact that humans are the only subjects that can be briefed before, and debriefed after, their participation in an experiment!

The possession of insight means that there is a special set of considerations that need to be taken into account when studying humans. Humans bring to any experiment some insight, however accurate or otherwise it might be, into what is going on. Some have said that doing experiments with humans is like a chemist trying to do experiments with only dirty test-tubes available. In neither case can the investigators have full knowledge of, nor control over, the material they are studying. The knowledge that a human brings to a situation can affect its outcome. A particularly good example of such an influence is the so-called 'placebo effect'. This term is dealt with more fully in Chapters 3 and 4, but we introduce you to an example of the effect here. Suppose a patient who is in pain is brought to hospital and given some capsules by an important-looking person in a white coat. It is often the case that the patient will report a reduction in the level of pain, irrespective of whether the capsules contained morphine or simply some quite arbitrary substance, such as sugar. It appears that a culture which accords power to people in white coats fosters an *expectation* of pain relief and this expectation can trigger physiological events in the body that act to counter pain.

Given that humans are so complex and have insights into their condition, what should be the approach of investigators trying to understand the human condition? There are several different options. One is to throw up our hands in despair, believing that we will never get answers to the question of what causes a person to behave as they do. There will thus remain some mystery and uncertainty. This might be the case, but it is still worth trying to understand as much as possible. Another approach is to divide up the responsibility, with biologists studying 'safe' areas such as hormones and neurons, and leave the more mysterious bits, such as the placebo effect, to psychologists and even mystics. The theme of SK220 is one of integration and holism, so we cannot afford to take either of these extreme positions. Rather, we need to confront the issue head-on and use all the skills we can muster to try to gain insight. A human being is a whole integrated person, with their physiology and psychology, whom we need to understand within their social context. The only way forward is to look to different disciplines and then to attempt some kind of synthesis. Thus, for example, the placebo effect is somewhat mysterious, but the evidence suggests that it is mediated via hormones and neurotransmitters. Thus although of necessity we need sometimes to be reductionist, to 'divide up' a person into bits, we still need to try to put them together again if we are to understand the whole.

The subsequent chapters of this book should demonstrate that this integrated approach is indeed possible. Chapter 2 looks at humans in the context of their sexual behaviour and reproduction. The chapter shows how a knowledge of basic biology (e.g. genes, chromosomes, hormones) is necessary to understand the process of human reproduction. However, in parallel with this essential reproductive biology, we consider the peculiarly human features of gender and reproduction. For example, humans have a gender identity, defined as 'the gender a person believes him- or herself to be'. Belief is, we imagine, something only humans possess. The richness of possibilities for human sexual development is apparent. Chapter 3 continues the story by addressing a very similar theme, this time looking in more detail at the complex set of factors which determine the nature and strength of sexual motivation in humans. In Chapter 4 we focus on pain. The reaction to tissue damage consists of some automatic withdrawal reflexes which are rather well understood in terms of the neural processes involved. These are very similar in different animal species. The chapter also looks at the peculiarities of pain perception in humans and considers the placebo effect in some depth. The subject of Chapter 5 is stress. Again we look for common features of the underlying processes as well as the peculiarities of humans. Our focus is upon emotional health, and particular lifestyle factors that can influence this. Aptly or not, the book closes with a chapter on sleep! Chapter 6 shows how much of our understanding of the question of *why* we sleep is gained from comparing sleep patterns in different animal species.

TV programme 4, *Healing the whole*, is directly relevant to this book, particularly Chapters 4 and 5.

CHAPTER 2
GENDER AND REPRODUCTION

2.1 Introduction – is sex necessary?

In this chapter we will be examining the areas of life that relate to reproduction. Sections 2.2 to 2.4 focus on the development by individuals of a sexual identity, and what this means in terms of their behaviour towards other individuals and within society as a whole. Sections 2.5 to 2.7 look at reproduction particularly from a woman's point of view since it is on women that most of the burden of reproduction falls.

Although sexual identity probably seems to most people to be a 'given', something that they are born with, it is in fact the result of many environmental influences acting upon an underlying genetic framework which may itself be subject to a certain amount of biological 'wobble'. We will be looking at all these factors – genetic, developmental and environmental – and putting together a picture of how they interact.

Why is sexuality necessary? You may remember studying in school biology classes small organisms which are not sexually differentiated (that is, in which two distinct forms are not required for reproduction) and which reproduce *asexually*, for example by splitting into two identical daughters. (It is conventional to refer to the products of asexual reproduction as daughters, because it is sometimes said that the 'default pathway' of development in many species is to a female type. You will learn more of this below.) Asexual reproduction indeed works well for many species, but, equally, according to classical theory, there are some advantages to a sexual mode of reproduction.

❏   Recall from Book 1, Chapter 4, the division that gives rise to germ cells. What is special about it?

■   The division is called *meiosis*, and it is a reduction division, halving the number of chromosomes. It also involves a process in which pieces of chromatids are exchanged, resulting in new combinations of genetic material.

The process of exchange of genetic material is called **recombination**, and it is important because it produces different combinations of alleles (different forms of a gene) in all the gametes (see Book 1, Chapter 4). This means that at fertilization the alleles contained in the egg are joined by a *different* set of alleles carried in by the sperm. Thus the new individual formed will carry a combination of alleles different from those carried by both its mother and its father.

❏   How does this differ from asexual reproduction?

■   In asexual reproduction the offspring are genetically identical to each other and to their single parent. Apart from the effects of occasional random mutations, all the members of all generations of an asexual family are identical.

On the face of it, genetic identity with other members of the species may not appear to be a disadvantage, although it might be rather boring. But it does mean that *all* the individuals will probably only be able to survive in the same small range of environments. With the allele combinations carried by the members of the population being limited, there is little flexibility or potential for adaptability, and a change in the environment, such as the advent of a new disease or a change in ambient temperature, may mean that all the individuals are wiped out. Of course, this argument could also apply to sexually reproducing species. But if at every generation new allele combinations are formed, the possibilities of greater flexibility, such as an improvement in the immune system to counteract a new disease or the production of enzymes able to operate at higher temperatures, are increased. Thus, over evolutionary timescales, natural selection will favour those individuals who can survive in changing environmental conditions. Sexual reproduction is one way of providing this variability within a species.

Some species have the option of reproducing sexually or asexually. For human beings, however, there is no option: if we want to reproduce, it has to be by sexual means. The importance of sex from an evolutionary point of view is perhaps mirrored in the importance it has at a day-to-day level for many individuals. In the rest of this chapter we will explore further the whole process. We start by looking at how a person becomes a member of a given sex, or gender. Note that 'sex' tends to be a biological description, whereas 'gender' has more sociological connotations.

2.2 How is gender identity established?

Gender identity is the gender a person believes himself or herself to be. For most people, this is self-evident and they have no problems with establishing their gender identity and following patterns of behaviour consistent with it. However, for a significant minority this area is fraught with difficulties, particularly regarding what is considered appropriate behaviour.

❏   Can you give an example of this?

■   There are many possible answers here, depending upon what you consider to be appropriate sexual behaviour. For example, you might have mentioned the distress experienced by some people in coming to terms with their homosexual or bisexual leanings, or the social problems sometimes experienced by heterosexual but highly sensitive men, or the disapproval experienced by some women who choose to remain childless.

Gender is assigned at birth by the appearance of the genitals (see Book 1, Chapter 6). This would seem to be the most obvious criterion, yet surprisingly the decision is not always clear-cut. As you will see below, male and female genitals are derived from the same embryonic tissues, and are merely put together in different ways. There are a number of cases where this process can go awry, leading, for example, to a tiny scrotum and penis so that the male individual appears to be female, or, conversely, to a clitoris grossly enlarged so as to appear to be a penis. Let us begin by looking at the biological basis of gender.

2.2.1 Genetic sex

❑   What is the genetic difference between women and men?

■   The body cells of women have two X chromosomes; those of men have one X and one Y chromosome.

The possession of a Y chromosome affects fetal development, turning off the female-directed pathways, and turning on the male-directed ones. In the absence of the Y chromosome, the undifferentiated gonad will proceed to develop along female lines. This is the basis for the statement that the female pathway is the default pathway for development, but it is *not* true to say that the undifferentiated form is female: development of a fetus into a functional female requires well-defined developmental events, just as development into a male does.

What is so special about the Y chromosome? In fact, the answer seems to be 'very little'. The human Y chromosome is very small, and represents considerably less than 1% of the human DNA.

❑   If DNA were equally distributed among all the chromosomes, what proportion would you expect the Y chromosome to carry?

■   There are 46 chromosomes, so an equal distribution of DNA among them would mean that $100\% \div 46 = 2.17\%$ of the DNA was carried by the Y chromosome.

This is in stark contrast to its opposite number, the X chromosome, which is relatively large and carries about 5% of the total DNA. Moreover, whereas most chromosomes are fairly constant in size, and loss of DNA from them can have serious if not lethal consequences, the size of the Y chromosome varies greatly among men, and it can lose significant amounts of DNA without loss of male function. The X and Y are pairing partners at cell division, even though they appear very different, unlike the other pairs of chromosomes which are virtually indistinguishable from each other. The X and Y pair by virtue of certain regions along the Y chromosome that are closely related to sequences in various parts of the X chromosome (see Figure 2.1). Sequences such as these, that are very similar, are called **homologous sequences**. Current theory has it that the Y chromosome evolved from a full-size X chromosome, with additions from other autosomes (non-sex chromosomes), and subsequent losses of areas that were not essential to its function. The pieces of the Y chromosome that pair with the X are necessary to prevent loss of the Y chromosome during division.

Examination of chromosomes from infertile men has shown that the male-determining gene on the Y chromosome lies on the short arm, and must be intact for male physical features to develop. The gene is called *Sry*, and is shown in Figure 2.1.

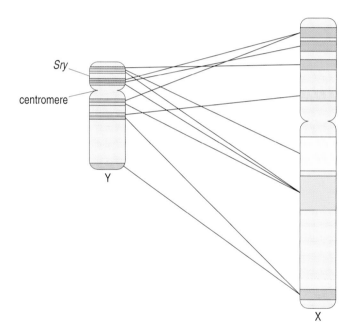

Figure 2.1   Map of the Y chromosome to show the position of the *Sry* gene, and some regions of homology with the X chromosome. Coloured regions on the X chromosome indicate regions where sequences in the correspondingly coloured regions of the Y chromosome are found.

It may seem strange that only one gene is needed to confer all male characteristics on an individual.

❑   Can you suggest how such a mechanism might work?

■   The *Sry* gene might act as a switch for differential gene expression, controlling a set of other 'male' genes.

The *Sry* gene belongs to a family of genes which code for proteins that can bind to specific base sequences in DNA. By analogy with other DNA binding proteins, it is suggested that the *Sry* protein might switch on or off genes situated close to where it binds, turning on 'male' genes, and turning off 'female' ones. This seems a plausible model, and it explains the scientific and clinical evidence. Whether it will turn out to be correct, though, remains to be seen.

2.2.2   Physical sex

What are the genes which the *Sry* protein allegedly controls? They fall into two categories: what we referred to above as 'male' genes, involved in processes such as testis determination and sperm production, and 'female' genes, which are those giving rise to the female reproductive tract, and which must be prevented from doing so if the individual is to be male.

The undifferentiated reproductive tract contains two sets of tubes, the mesonephric, or *Wolffian* ducts, and the paramesonephric, or *Müllerian* ducts (see Figure 2.2). You met these as mesonephroi in Book 1, Chapter 5. As the female develops, the Wolffian ducts regress, and the Müllerian ducts grow to form the Fallopian tubes, uterus and cervix. Conversely, in the male the Wolffian ducts are what develops into the vasa deferentia (singular: vas deferens), and the Müllerian ducts regress under the influence of *anti-Müllerian hormone*, encoded by a gene apparently activated by the *Sry* protein. Anti-Müllerian hormone is made specifically by the Sertoli cells in the developing testis, so in the absence of a testis the Müllerian duct will persist, and female structures will be formed. The testis also produces high levels of androgens from the Leydig cells (think back to Book 1, Chapter 4). The androgens affect not only the development of male reproductive structures, but also brain development (Chapter 3 in this book).

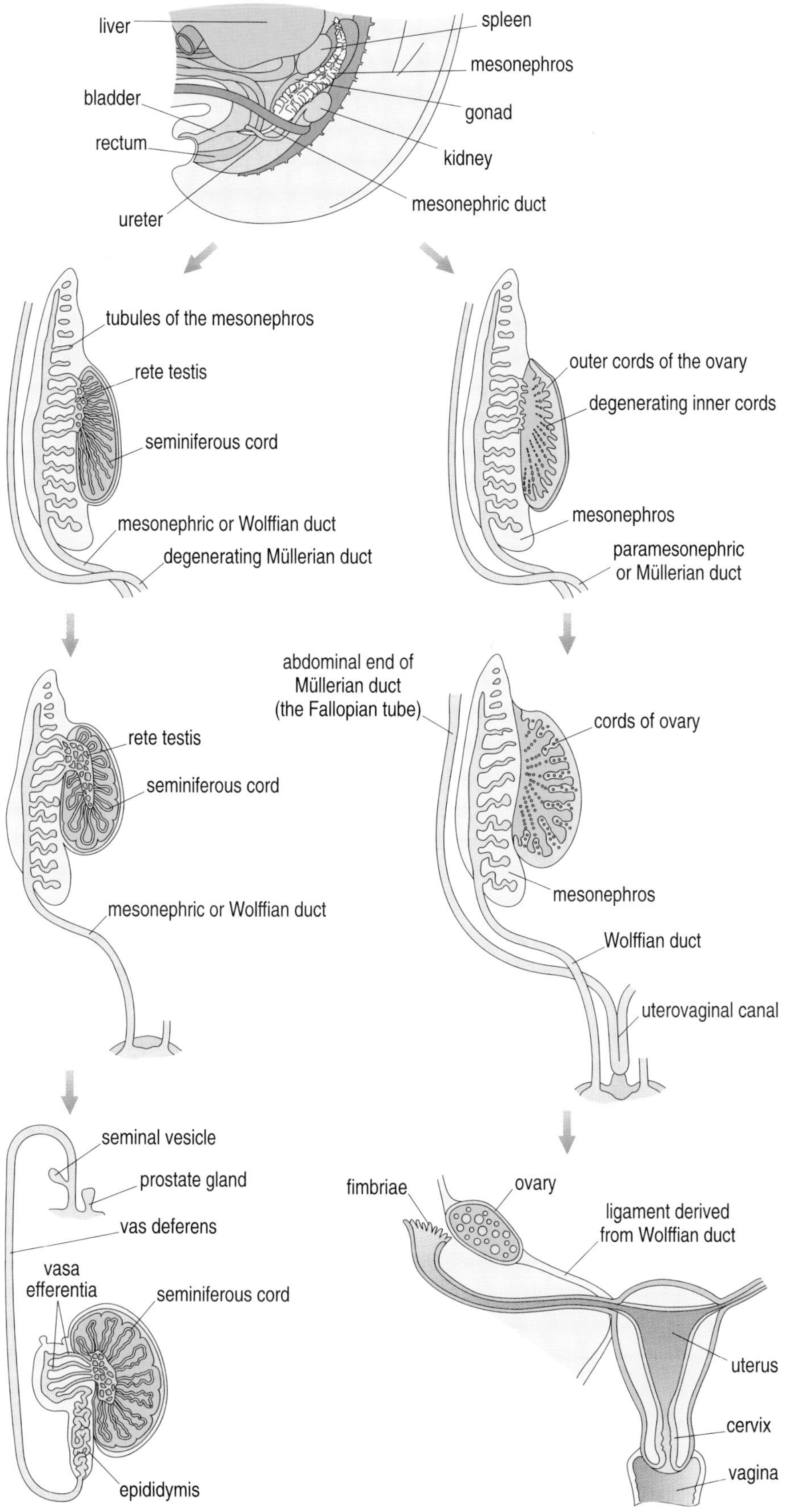

Figure 2.2 Development of male (left) and female (right) reproductive organs from the Wolffian and Müllerian ducts.

Since sexual identity is assigned by the appearance of the genitals, it is important to understand how these are formed. A comparative scheme is shown in Figure 2.3. To begin with, the genitals are identical in both male and female, and consist of a genital tubercle, genital swellings, and urethral folds. As growth proceeds, in the female the urethral folds and genital swellings remain separate, giving rise to the inner and outer labia, and the genital tubercle shrinks to form the clitoris. However, in the presence of testosterone (the main androgen) the urethral folds and the genital swellings fuse, forming the scrotum, and the genital tubercle expands, forming the penis. The urethral folds 'wrap around', to form the tubular urethra. In the absence of androgens, the primordial structures will take the female pathway of development.

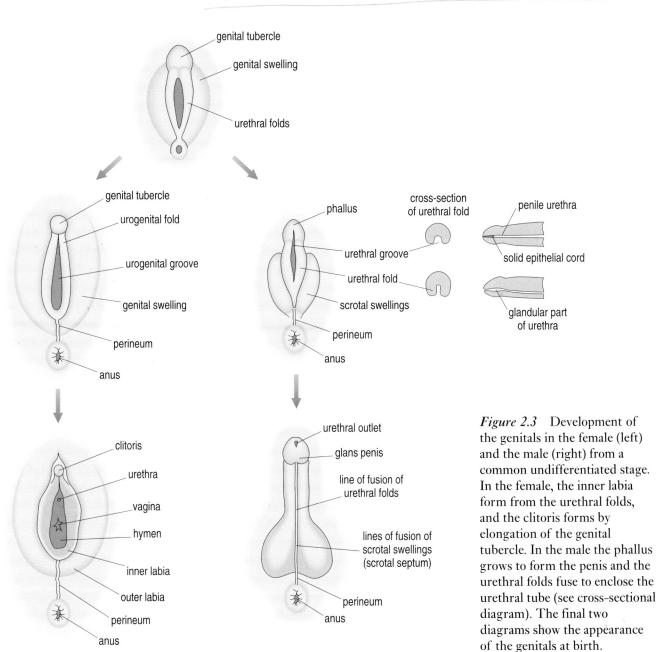

Figure 2.3 Development of the genitals in the female (left) and the male (right) from a common undifferentiated stage. In the female, the inner labia form from the urethral folds, and the clitoris forms by elongation of the genital tubercle. In the male the phallus grows to form the penis and the urethral folds fuse to enclose the urethral tube (see cross-sectional diagram). The final two diagrams show the appearance of the genitals at birth.

As you might imagine, it is very important in the male that the primordia become exposed to testosterone at the correct time.

❑   What would you predict might happen if testosterone were absent during the critical period?

■   The primordia would develop along the female pathway.

This is illustrated in Figure 2.4. It sometimes happens if for some reason testosterone is produced late, or in inadequate quantities, by an XY fetus. Depending upon the precise timing, or the severity of the defect, the appearance of the genitals in the new-born baby can lead to an assignation of gender that conflicts with the genetic sex, for example, an XY individual being assigned female gender. This can lead to severe problems at adolescence, when genetic sex and gender identity come into conflict. In this course we can only speculate about the psychological effects of having been brought up as one gender, only to find that one belongs in fact to the other, although we will consider an example of this later. This brings us to another facet of gender identity: gender role and sexual preferences.

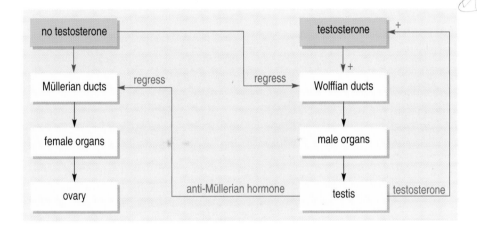

Figure 2.4   Hormonal influences on the development of reproductive organs in males and females. In the absence of testosterone, the Müllerian ducts develop into female organs, and the Wolffian ducts regress. However, in the presence of testosterone, the Wolffian ducts develop along the male pathway. The testis produces more testosterone, which reinforces this pathway, and also anti-Müllerian hormone, which causes the Müllerian ducts to regress. '+' indicates stimulation.

2.2.3   Gender role and sexual preference

Gender role is the behaviour of an individual to convey her or his gender identity. This includes behaviour related to sexuality, but is not restricted to it: for example, the preference of some girls to engage in so-called tomboyish behaviour, rather than playing with dolls, is part of their gender role, and signals that their role-playing does not necessarily include home-making and motherhood. **Sexual preference** is the preference shown by an individual for members of one or other gender in a sexual context. For example, a heterosexual woman has a sexual preference for men; a homosexual man also has a sexual preference for men. Sexual preference is clear-cut for some people, but less so for others.

The gender role will be strongly influenced initially by the gender assignation at birth.

❑   Why?

◼   Parents and other people treat boys and girls differently.

Though many people might take this for granted, the issues surrounding it are complex. In part it is no doubt due to adults' expectations of how little girls and little boys should behave. Also, common parental experience suggests that boys and girls *are* different, and demand to be treated differently. This is perhaps not surprising given that some male and female hormones and parts of their brains are different. Whatever the reason, growing children are subjected to a barrage of reinforcement – much of it unwitting – of gender role behaviour, 'Big boys don't cry' or 'Nice girls don't fight' being common examples. From a very early age, children know how to play their gender roles: they understand what is considered to be acceptable dress and behavioural patterns for each gender. They are aware of belonging to a 'club' that excludes about half the world, and they are generally very proud of this distinction, each sex believing that they are the best, and that the other is at the very least a little odd. This too is part of the gender role.

Understanding the socially acceptable behaviour patterns associated with gender roles leads almost automatically to an expectation that when they grow up, boys and girls will become men and women with sexual preferences that are 'correct'; that is, for the opposite sex. The onset of puberty is a fairly turbulent time for most individuals, and if one abruptly realizes that one's sexual preferences do not lie in the expected direction, this adds significantly to the difficulties.

In the context of gender roles and subsequent sexual preferences, some rather surprising evidence has come from a study of a group of people in the Dominican Republic. A commonly inherited disorder among these people is a deficiency in testosterone production. Affected boys have external genitals that look female, and they are assigned female gender at birth and are raised as girls. However, at puberty, the increased production of testosterone allows their genitals to become masculinized. The clitoris enlarges to become a functional penis, beard growth starts, and the voice breaks. The boys appear to reverse their gender identity almost overnight, with little difficulty.

❑   What does this suggest about gender assignation at birth?

◼   It suggests that it is unimportant in the development of adult gender identity among these people.

However, the situation is not so clear-cut. The condition is relatively common, and the boys are given the name 'Guevodoces' ('Penis-at-twelves'), suggesting that society is well aware of the condition and its effects. Also, it becomes apparent during childhood, well before adolescence, that testes are present. It is likely that as soon as doubt arises as to their true gender, these boys may well be treated differently from normal girls. This example illustrates the different approaches taken by different societies in their assignment of gender. Whereas this Dominican society seems to adopt a flexible approach to the Guevodoces (as do the Guevodoces themselves), in other societies this might not occur, and the gender role adopted during childhood would play a more defining role in the gender identity finally assumed.

Summary of Section 2.2

1   An individual's gender identity is affected by their genetic sex, their physical sex, and their gender role. It does not necessarily dictate their sexual preference.

2   Genetic sex is determined by the presence or absence of a Y chromosome, carried by genetic males.

3   The Y chromosome is the counterpart of the X chromosome, and is partly derived from it. Much of it is unimportant; but the *Sry* gene is essential for the development of maleness.

4   The reproductive tract of males and females is derived from the same embryonic tissues, which develop in different ways under the influence of hormones.

5   Individuals adopt behaviour patterns appropriate to their gender identity. There is a strong cultural component in this.

2.3 Puberty: getting ready to reproduce

Puberty is the name given to the stage of development when an individual becomes able to reproduce. The entire process takes several years to accomplish. Much of this time is spent in growth: there are lower limits to the body size at which reproduction is possible. The growth spurt is generally taken to be the first sign of adolescence, and its onset occurs in most children at *around* the same age, early teenage, tending to be earlier in girls than in boys. The final achievement of physical adult status is marked in girls by the advent of the first menstrual period (this event is called **menarche**), and in boys by the first ejaculation. This latter may seem a rather arbitrary criterion, but in fact is the only functional test which can be easily applied. Moreover, it, like menstruation, is an event which leaves individuals themselves in no doubt as to their reproductive status. Over the last century or so the average age at which these events occur has dropped, as shown for girls in Figure 2.5. This pattern is repeated in many countries, so it is unlikely to be due to any country-specific phenomenon such as a new public health measure, and more likely to be due to some factor that has affected all the countries in which the effect is seen to a similar extent. Based on animal studies which we need not detail here, the trigger for adolescence is nutrition-related.

Figure 2.5 Trend towards an earlier age at menarche in developed countries between 1840 and 1960.

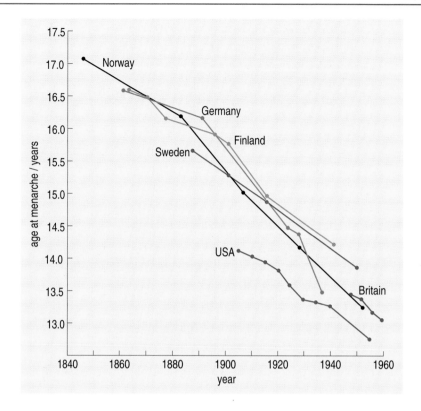

(*Finland*: 1862–1915, hospital patients, Helsinki, from Malmio (1919) and Vara (1943); 1941, medical practice and health visitor inquiries, all Finland, age at interrogation 17 to 27 only, from Simell (1952). *Sweden*: 1886–1915, hospital patients, Lund and Stockholm, from Essen-Möller (quoted in Lenner, 1944), Lundh (1925), Samuelson (1942) and Lenner (1944) (hospital data of last two pooled for value at 1915); 1950, schoolchildren, estimated from data of Romanus (1952). *Norway*: 1844–1881, from Backman (1948); 1907, Oslo hospital patients, from Skerlj (1939); 1928–1952, Oslo schoolchildren, data of Schiötz (1930), and Kiil (1953) fitted by probits. *Germany*: 1860–1928, hospital patients, various towns, successively from Schlichting (1880), Heyn (1920) and Schaeffer (1908) pooled, Risopoulos (1936), Scheibner (1938); 1937, schoolchildren, S. W. Germany, probits fitted to data of Ley (1938). *Great Britain*: 1948–60, schoolchildren, probits, successively S. England, from Wilson & Sutherland (1950b), Edinburgh from Provis & Ellis (1955), Bristol from Wofinden & Smallwood (1958), London from Scott (1961). *USA*: 1905–1940, University of South Carolina entrants, from Mills (1950), 1960 estimated. *Denmark*: 1950, Copenhagen schoolchildren, probits, from Bojlén, Rasch & Weis-Bentzon (1954).)

The level of nutrition, at least in developed countries, has generally improved over the last hundred or so years (although see Book 3, Chapter 7, for a discussion of dietary quality). If the data represented in Figure 2.5 are plotted to show body weight at menarche, then an interesting fact emerges: body weight at menarche has remained at a fairly constant 47 kg over the time period studied (Figure 2.6). In boys the weight at which puberty occurs is about 55 kg. All that has changed over the years is the time taken to achieve these weights – better nutrition means that the weight is achieved at a younger age. Furthermore, there seems also to be a critical weight linked to the onset of the growth spurt.

❑   What does this suggest about the trigger for puberty?

■   It suggests that the trigger for puberty is some event which is related to body weight, and that, once the process has been triggered, it progresses in a way that is also linked to increasing body weight.

Although there is some evidence, based on the failure of anorexic teenagers to menstruate, to support this hypothesis, it has not yet been verified, and it has not proved easy to use the hypothesis to *predict* the time of either the onset of the growth spurt or menarche.

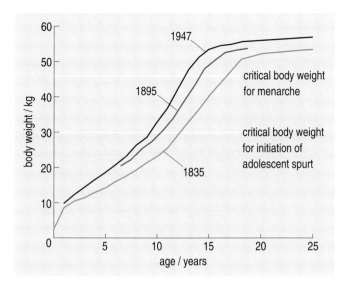

Figure 2.6   Graph showing the weight increase with age of three populations of girls in 1835, 1895 and 1947. White lines show the critical weights for the onset of the growth spurt and for menarche.

2.3.1   Development of secondary sexual characteristics

During the growth spurt, the individual increases in height, and also to some extent in girth, although these two parameters may not increase in a coordinated way, leading to the observation that teenagers tend to be gawky and out of proportion. Other changes, less obvious to a cursory glance, are to the genitals: in boys the scrotum enlarges and the penis lengthens and thickens, and in girls the labia and clitoris enlarge.

❑   What is the developmental relationship between these tissues?

■   They are derived from the same embryonic cells. This means that they are likely to be responsive to similar hormonal signals.

Adolescent boys are often preoccupied with the size of their penis. The corresponding worry, that their genitals are not big enough, is not generally experienced by girls, who tend to worry instead about the size of their breasts. Presumably this difference arises because the breasts are sited in a very obvious place, whereas the vulva is located in a position which makes it difficult to 'compare and contrast', in the way that boys are said to do. In fact, from a biological point of view, any size of penis that can maintain an erection and deposit semen in a vagina is perfectly adequate. But humans are more than biological equipment, and the peer-group pressure in this respect leads many teenage boys and girls to wonder whether they will be 'real' men or women. You will learn more of sexual psychology in Chapter 3.

These changes to the genitals are actually regarded as secondary sexual characteristics, and are an accompaniment to internal changes to the reproductive systems in both sexes, the primary sexual characteristics, which we will examine in a moment.

❑   Do you know any other secondary sexual characteristics?

◼   Growth of pubic hair, breast development and voice breaking are some well-known ones.

Body hair, including of course pubic hair, occurs in sex-specific patterns. In women it is largely confined to the axillae (armpits) and pubic region, while in men a much more extensive pattern involving chest, arms, legs and back may be found. Men also grow facial hair.

As described above, breast growth is to girls what penile growth is to boys. Although the size of a breast bears no relation to its ability to produce milk – large breasts are mostly fat – large breasts, like large penises, are perceived as status symbols in some societies. Furthermore, their involvement in sexual arousal and their prominent position can cause embarrassment to an adolescent girl, much as the curious sounds produced by a breaking voice can do to a boy, although probably worse. We will look at breast development in more detail in Section 2.6.1 below.

Male voices break because the larynx enlarges under the influence of testosterone. As the larynx gets bigger, so too do its muscles, resulting in deeper tones developing. The large larynx can be seen as the Adam's apple, present in men but not in women.

Rather more subtle, but still secondary, sexual characteristics are features such as differential growth patterns to establish the characteristic male and female body shapes, as shown in Figure 2.7. Males increase muscle development, particularly around the shoulders and chest, while females begin to lay down fat deposits at specific sites such as thighs and buttocks, to give a 'womanly', more rounded outline. This is underpinned by the different shape of the pelvis in both sexes.

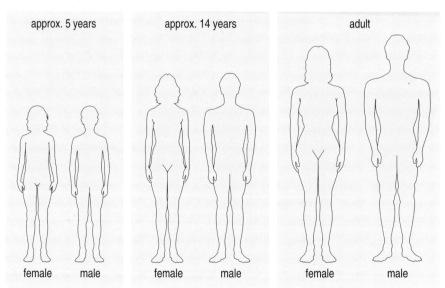

Figure 2.7   Outlines of developing male and female shapes from a 'child-like' outline.

2.3.2   Development of primary sexual characteristics

We have discussed some of the obvious features of puberty; let us now go on to look at the primary sexual characteristics.

❑   What are the fundamental changes necessary for reproduction?

■   Changes resulting in the production of functional eggs and sperm.

At this point, you may find it helpful to look back to Book 1, Chapter 4, where you learned about the processes involved in gametogenesis.

❑   Recall the class of compound controlling gametogenesis.

■   Hormones.

Puberty is accompanied by huge surges in reproductive hormones and growth hormone. For example, testosterone, which is present in the blood of young boys and girls at levels below 10 ng per 100 ml (remember that a nanogram is a thousand-millionth of a gram), is found at 240 ng per 100 ml in adolescent boys. Adolescent girls also show a rise in testosterone level, but it is less, achieving only 40 ng per 100 ml. Girls, however, experience a rise in oestrogens secreted by the ovaries, and this is what controls breast development. FSH and LH levels (follicle-stimulating hormone, and lutenizing hormone; see Book 1, Chapter 4) rise by a similar amount in males and females, as shown in Figure 2.8.

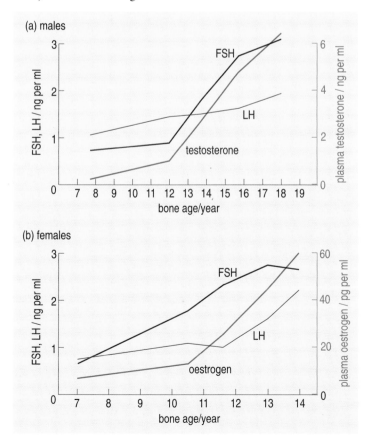

Figure 2.8   Oestrogen, testosterone, LH and FSH plasma concentrations at various stages of puberty in (a) boys and (b) girls. Bone age is assessed by examining X-rays of hand, knee and elbow, and comparing them with standards in the general population. It is an index of physical maturity, and a better match for development of secondary sexual characteristics than chronological age.

❑   Where are FSH and LH made?

■   In the pituitary gland.

LH and FSH secretion are controlled by pulses of GnRH (gonadotropin-releasing hormone) from the hypothalamus (a region of the brain which you learned about in Book 2). This in turn is controlled by secretions from the gonads themselves, including, but not confined to, the sex steroids like testosterone. Testosterone exerts a negative feedback effect on the production of GnRH, and lowers quite considerably the amount of circulating LH. It also reduces the levels of FSH, but not to such a great extent: another hormone, called *inhibin*, is also involved in FSH control. Inhibin is produced by Sertoli cells in the testis, and its production is linked to spermatogenesis. This is illustrated in Figure 2.9.

❑   What mechanism is this an example of?

■   This is another example of negative feedback.

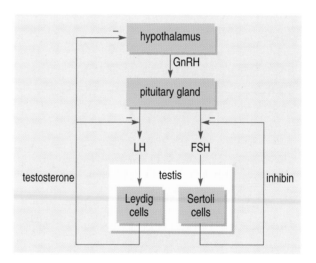

Figure 2.9   Control of male sex hormones.

It is relatively easy to see how these systems operate to control gametogenesis in the adult, but what happens at puberty? In childhood, these hormones are kept at low, fairly constant levels; in the adult the levels are higher and fluctuate according to daily or monthly rhythms, as shown in Figure 2.10. At puberty, some switch must occur to change the childhood pattern to an adult one, but so far the nature of the switch remains obscure.

Whatever the mechanism for activating the hormonal changes at puberty, its effect is to raise the levels of several circulating hormones according to a specific pattern. The main result of this is, as you have seen, to activate and then to maintain the processes of egg and sperm production. But there is more to reproduction than merely producing gametes. Since general, and

(a)

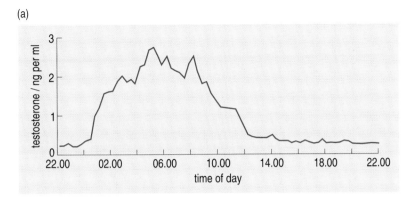

not just genital, metabolism is affected by puberty, it is not surprising that there are other more generalized features associated with it. The most widely experienced one is probably the increase in secretion of oil from sebaceous glands in the skin. This leads to greasy hair and spots, and, together with an increase in appetite and an increased desire to sleep for prolonged periods, is one of the most widely recognized signs of adolescence.

❑   Why do you think appetite increases?

■   To supply energy and nutrients to a rapidly growing body.

❑   Why might more sleep be required?

■   Perhaps to make up for the tiring process of growth. But it might also be related to the increased secretion of hormones that occurs during sleep (see Figure 2.10a).

2.3.3   The function of secondary sexual characteristics

Why do we have secondary sexual characteristics? Features such as breast size and body hair are very obvious differences that distinguish adults from children, that is, that mark out prospective mates. What the precise significance of this might be, however, is largely unknown. The most widely publicized theory about secondary sexual characteristics states that they are involved in increasing the attraction of one sex for the other. According to the theory, an individual who most closely resembles the 'ideal' for their sex (rounded body shape for women; tall and broad shouldered for men) will have the best chance of mating and having many children. Furthermore, the theory would have it that body hair is sited in such a way as to maximize odour, and odour is an important component of sexual attraction.

Figure 2.10   (a) Circadian cycles of testosterone in an adolescent boy. The high levels during sleep are said to account for the 'nocturnal emissions' – that is, ejaculations during sleep – experienced by many adolescent boys. Note that women also show circadian patterns of some hormones.
(b) Monthly cycles of oestrogen, progestogen, testosterone, FSH and LH in an adult woman.
O = ovulation; M = menstruation.

(b)

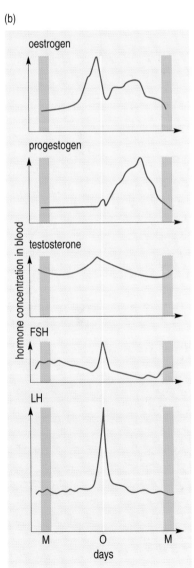

Think of a sexual characteristic such as broad shoulders, or large breasts. (No, this isn't a joke.) How might you establish the size that people find 'ideal'? How would you distinguish between your respondents' sexual preferences, and current fashion? Is there a difference? From doing this activity, do you think the theory outlined above is likely to be correct?

The theory may be correct in part, but it has limited plausibility. All men have shoulders and all women have buttocks, but the variety of shapes and sizes found suggests that collectively we are not very fussy about what shapes we find acceptable in a partner. Also, body hair is the physical feature over which we probably have the most control – anyone can choose to have a shave or a haircut, and from time immemorial there have been different fashions for hair length, beards, and removal of body hair, without any obvious impact on general reproductive performance.

Thus the theory appears flawed. Indeed, it is possible that, for reasons unclear to us at present, secondary sexual characteristics are *necessary* consequences of the hormonal effects that control the primary characteristics. The tissues have to be sensitive to sex hormones to fulfil their functions – perhaps this sensitivity means that they automatically develop as they do, without a purpose. In any case, it seems unlikely that any theory involving this part of human activity could ever be fully validated as the experiments would be technically and ethically difficult to carry out.

Summary of Section 2.3

1   Puberty is marked by the menarche in girls and the first ejaculation in boys.

2   The trigger for puberty, and for the growth spurt that precedes it, is associated with a particular body weight.

3   The visible changes at puberty are the secondary sexual characteristics; the primary characteristics are the production of functional eggs and sperm.

4   Both primary and secondary sexual characteristics develop under the influence of hormones.

2.4 Puberty: growing up in the wider world

Among the other distinguishing features of adolescence are major behavioural changes, driven by the physical changes just described, and it is to these that we turn next. The transition from childhood to adulthood is a major milestone in people's lives. In many cultures it is surrounded by ceremony, which can range from genital mutilation to having a big party.

From being a child, largely dependent on the immediate family, the individual begins to develop autonomy and social status, and must learn to take their place in society at large. For many people, the trouble with adolescence is that reality is a long way from expectations: either they are forcibly thrust into situations which they feel unprepared to cope with, or else they are restrained and not given as much 'freedom' as they would like. It has been said by several commentators, including the anthropologist Margaret Mead, who carried out pioneering research in this field, that in cultures where there are very specific rites of passage during adolescence, growing up seems a much less traumatic process than it appears to be in our society, where adolescence is not celebrated in any formal way. Almost all the rites of passage described in the literature apply exclusively to young men, and most involve some kind of physical test of strength. One suggestion for the origin of these ceremonies is that they mimic the blood and pain experienced by women when they are menstruating. Certainly in many societies there is very powerful imagery associated with menstruation, so rites of passage might represent a 'me too' approach to this symbolism for men. Alternatively, it might mean that more effort is required to assimilate boys into a stable society.

❑   Can you think of examples from modern British society where tests of physical strength and ability to endure pain are carried out?

■   Many informal 'nights out with the lads' involve physical or psychological violence. Withstanding the effects of a poison – alcohol – is widely seen as a test of manhood. Achieving greater mobility, by passing a driving test, or simply by joy-riding, is also a status symbol. Perhaps the most ritualized test of strength involves sport.

2.4.1 Courtship behaviour

During adolescence and, some would say, during much of adulthood too, a good deal of time and effort is devoted to learning the correct behaviour patterns and signals to attract members of the opposite sex. (These patterns are generally learned by everybody, even if their own preferences are for members of their own sex.) **Courtship behaviour** is the biological term applied to the behaviour patterns used by individuals (of any species) as a prelude to mating. Sexuality is a very important part of most people's make-up, and many individuals, particularly adolescents, spend much of their time thinking about sex; this tends to be reinforced by peer-group pressure and the media. However, to avoid physical injuries and unwanted pregnancies it is important that our powerful sexual feelings should be channelled into socially acceptable paths. All societies have extensive and complex rules about sexual behaviour, and these must be learned by all members of the society, even if they are not sexually active members of it. The rules are complicated because they are not just about which individuals may engage in sexual activities, but also about social structure and economics. The rather glib explanation of sexual roles as being based on 'man the hunter' and 'woman the home-maker' is a huge over-simplification of thousands of years of social evolution, and, indeed, is not readily applicable to all modern societies. Much has been written about courtship behaviour and the rituals surrounding the progression from mutual attraction signalled by eye contact and other body language through to full sexual intercourse, but space constraints mean that we cannot discuss it further here.

2.4.2 Sexual maturity

Full sexual maturity – as signalled in men by ejaculates containing functional sperm, and in women by menstrual cycles that include ovulations of fertile eggs – often precedes emotional maturity (whatever that is) and the legal age of consent. For this reason, and also through choice (see Book 1, Chapter 4), it is usual for most people to spend several years in a state when they are *able* to reproduce, but are not actually doing so. They may or may not be sexually active during this time with one or more partners; many will relieve their sexual urges through masturbation.

Sex drive does not appear to be constant in either sex. As you will learn in Chapter 3, it can be affected by many factors including age, diet, state of health, tiredness, stimuli from the immediate surroundings, and presence or absence of a desired partner – that is, a conducive environment. In women it also appears to be affected by cyclic hormonal influences. A traditional, biological reductionist explanation for this is that women desire sex most at the times when it is most likely to get them pregnant.

❏   When is this?

■   Around the time of ovulation, in the middle of the menstrual cycle (taking day 1 as the first day of bleeding).

However, this is in fact contrary to many women's experience.

❏   Do you find this surprising?

■   We hope you do not. As this course has tried to show, humans are much more than bags of chemicals, at the mercy of deterministic hormonal influences.

Although some women do indeed desire sex most in the middle of their cycles, others prefer it before, during or after menstruation – precisely when they are *least* likely to become pregnant. In other words, women are individuals and respond to various cues in individual ways.

But no matter how much we might like to rise above our biological nature, fundamentally we are biological beings, and *to some extent* we *must* respond in an automatic way to hormones in our bodies.

❏   From systems you have studied elsewhere in this course, give an
        example of how human behaviour is influenced by hormones.

■   When blood sugar, regulated by insulin and glucagon, is low, we feel
        tired and hungry. When secretion of antidiuretic hormone is
        suppressed, we produce a lot of urine and feel the urge to urinate.
        No doubt you thought of other examples.

In view of this, it would be surprising if the levels of sex hormones did not
affect our behaviour too. Indeed, sexual urges in general are attributed
(rightly or wrongly) to levels of testosterone. The point to emphasize here
is that our behaviour is certainly *affected* by hormones, but we are in most
cases able to exercise some control over our feelings, and modify our
behaviour.

❏   How can the behaviour you identified in the previous question be
        voluntarily modified?

■   Even when we feel hungry, we can wait until the next meal before we
        eat; the urge to urinate can be controlled until an appropriate
        moment; your own example.

One well-known effect of cyclic patterns of hormone production in women
is the occurrence of the so-called pre-menstrual syndrome (PMS).
Symptoms of this include fluid retention and a feeling of bloating,
abdominal pain, headaches, nausea, emotional swings and general
irritability, and their severity ranges from imperceptible to seriously
debilitating. PMS has been a controversial area, particularly relating to
employment, precisely because women are affected by it to varying extents.
This, of course, applies to menstruation too. Although some women appear
to be little affected by either PMS or menstruation, others suffer so
severely from the symptoms that they feel unable to carry out their normal
daily activities, and prefer to rest in seclusion.

Think about the problems faced by employers in employing staff who may
need one or more days off each month on a regular (or irregular) basis.
Should they be employed at all? Should they be paid less than an employee
who does not need regular time off? Should a few days per month off work
be written into every employee's contract? If possible, discuss this issue
with others.

We hope that thinking about this matter, and perhaps discussing it with
other people, has made you realize how difficult it is to cater, in terms of
legislation, for people's individuality. Perhaps what is required is a
fundamentally different approach to employment!

Summary of Section 2.4

1   Puberty is a time of great physical and emotional changes.

2   Many cultures engage in specific rites of passage for adolescence.

3   All societies have complex rules about courtship behaviour and mate choice.

4   Sexually mature people often have powerful sex drives; societies also have rules to channel these in appropriate ways.

5   Hormones can have profound effects on behaviour.

2.5 Pregnancy – well-being or dis-ease?

From a biological point of view, the attainment of sexual maturity is just a prelude to the main business of life: reproduction. For humans, particularly women, this involves a big commitment, both physical and emotional, and the following sections focus on reproduction from a woman's point of view. We start with pregnancy.

Once a pregnancy is established, a woman experiences fundamental changes in her feeling of well-being. These may be positive or negative. Of course, this will depend in part on whether or not the pregnancy is welcomed, but other factors may be involved too. Some of these may be physical – for example, the woman may suffer from severe morning sickness, which may reduce her feeling of well-being to sub-zero – but others may be acting more at the level of emotions. If a baby is likely to be a threat to financial or domestic security, then, even if the pregnancy is welcomed, the mother will probably be worrying about the future. Often physical and emotional factors are in conflict: the mother may be extremely worried, but may be physically blooming, or may be feeling physically poorly, yet quite cheerful. And, of course, these pregnancy-induced changes will be overlaid onto a background of the woman's 'normal' situation, with its own positive and negative aspects, any or all of which can interact with the new factors. In short, it is almost impossible to predict how any woman will feel when pregnant. If the woman has a regular partner, his feelings, and his reactions to her feelings, will also be factors to consider. Small wonder that most couples feel the need to redefine the terms of their relationship once they start a family. Yet this is the time at which it is least easy to do so. Many couples can make compromises on the understanding that the pregnancy, and the accompanying emotional surges, will not last for ever. But others find it difficult if not impossible to reach a working agreement. It is socially unacceptable for a couple to split up during a pregnancy; even in the worst of situations, they are supposed to see it through in the expectation that matters will improve when the baby arrives. In particular, the woman is perceived to be vulnerable and in need of both emotional and physical support, and a man who leaves his partner at this time is particularly reviled. This is one example of the complex social rules which have evolved around reproductive behaviour, as we mentioned above. And this brings us to a particularly fraught topic: that of sexual behaviour during pregnancy.

It is a common experience of pregnant women that their libido – their desire for sex – increases greatly during pregnancy (Stoppard, 1986, p. 68). This is probably the result of several factors, including an increased level of circulating sex hormones, an increased volume of blood (making the woman feel warm and energetic), and, at some very fundamental level, a feeling of successful achievement and pride. There is also no fear of becoming pregnant at this time! Libido is a complex phenomenon, and is under the influence of many things, but a strong component is the feel-good factor of self-worth. For many women, pregnancy can represent the major achievement of their lives, and very few can go through the process of making a new human being without feeling a little smug.

Whatever the reason for it, some couples find that during pregnancy their sex lives are better than ever before, and this may be an important mechanism for bringing them together at what may otherwise be a rather difficult time. But this is not the case for all couples. The man may not appreciate his partner's increased sex drive; the woman's swelling abdomen may make it difficult to find a mutually comfortable position; the woman may feel embarrassment about her changing body; her partner may not find her attractive; and there may be worries on the part of both partners that the baby might be harmed by sex (even though it is widely accepted that, during a normal pregnancy, there is no risk of harm coming to the embryo or fetus during the course of 'normal' sexual activities – penetration and female orgasm will not *per se* induce a miscarriage). Whether or not their sex lives are satisfactory, some couples find that pregnancy induces in them feelings of 'togetherness', which could be important in helping them to overcome the stresses of new parenthood, and provide a settled environment for their baby.

2.5.1   The end of the beginning: labour and birth

Towards the end of pregnancy, sexual activity drops markedly for most couples. Generally, a woman will feel uncomfortable at this stage: she will be carrying a lot of extra weight which may cause problems such as back-ache, oedema (swelling) and varicose veins as her body struggles to maintain normal activities. The increased pressure in her abdomen may interfere with digestive movements and give her indigestion, and will also mean that it is difficult for her to breathe deeply. In spite of this, she will remain active and, in the main, carry out her normal daily activities. You may have heard stories of women in the developing world who give birth in the fields as a mere interruption of their agricultural activities; most women do not have to do this, but the principle remains the same!

Because the time of onset of labour cannot be predicted (see Book 1, Chapter 6), the most practical approach for most women is to carry on as normal until it becomes apparent that the baby is definitely coming. Indeed, many women report that physical activity can ease labour pains. Movement of any kind, including simply walking about, is generally found to be very helpful in easing pain. For labour, women find positions in which the pain is more manageable, and may wish to alternate these positions with bouts of walking around. Pictorial evidence from around the world shows quite a variety of positions commonly adopted for labour (see Figure 2.11). However, in the UK, there has been a tendency for childbirth to be 'medicalized', that is, treated more as a disease than as a natural process. The obstetric practices of the 19th century, and the first half of the 20th, frowned on any position that restricted the doctor's view of proceedings: women were literally confined to their beds, lying on their backs. This is, in fact, probably the worst possible position for giving birth, since a woman in this position does not even have the benefit of gravity to help the baby out (see Figure 2.12), but it was easier for the obstetrician to see what was going on. Nowadays, the trend is to give women as much power as possible in their own deliveries, and midwives are happy (or at least willing!) to get down on the floor with the labouring mother so as to examine her without interrupting her efforts. The only exception to this is if a problem arises, and close monitoring of mother or fetus is required. Monitoring fetal heart rate, the best measure of fetal distress, can be done through the mother's abdominal wall. Modern fetal heart monitors are portable and do not interfere with the mother's mobility, but many hospitals still have the old-fashioned type involving a strap around the mother's abdomen, attached to a large machine. Being attached to one of these seriously limits mobility during labour.

(a)

(b)

FIG. 2. — Labor Scene among the **Wakambas**. (Western portion of Central Africa.)

(c)

(d)

Figure 2.11   Delivery in various cultures: (a) birth in New Guinea; (b) labour among the Wakambas (Western part of Central Africa); (c) birth in the UK, 1970s; (d) home birth, mid-16th century (Gordon, 1993).

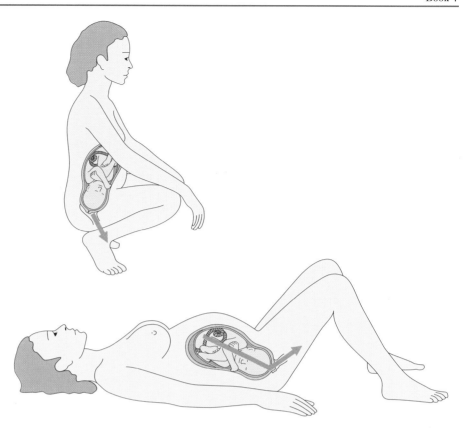

Figure 2.12   The effect of gravity on labour.

What causes pain during labour? It is, of course, the effort required to expel a fairly large baby through a fairly small opening. At some point in our evolution, humans became upright, and the adoption of a bipedal stance (walking on two legs) involves a trade-off. An upright posture leads to a change in the shape of the pelvis, but this narrows the birth canal. Our large, brainy human heads make matters worse (see Book 1, Chapter 6). The uterus walls, made of smooth muscle, are capable of delivering enormously powerful contractions, but, as you have seen in Book 2, muscular contraction involves chemical reactions which have a waste product, lactate. If the lactate is not removed by the blood, it will accumulate and cause pain (muscular cramps) and tissue damage. The amount of lactate produced by the strong, lengthy contractions needed to expel the baby accumulates quite significantly, and causes a lot of pain. Furthermore, the effort required to carry out the contractions is very tiring, and this makes the pain harder to bear. It helps to be physically fit to give birth: as you have already seen, increased fitness leads to better removal of lactate, and a fit person will get tired less quickly. Uterine contractions are intermittent, and come with increasing frequency as labour progresses. Indeed, the increasing frequency and duration of the contractions is a good indicator of true labour, rather than the Braxton–Hicks practice contractions (Book 1, Chapter 6) that occur throughout the latter part of pregnancy. The pain of contractions is not necessarily localized to the uterus: depending on the position of the fetus it may begin as severe back-ache.

Many women attend antenatal classes, during the course of which they will be taught the mechanics of the birth process, and how to cope with the pain they will experience. Generally, an understanding of what is happening to them will relieve women's fear and stress, and this is perceived as a good thing, because fear is known to exacerbate pain. But no amount of theory can prepare women for the actuality of labour, and the physical and emotional sides of the process. In the developed world, women are fortunate in having the option of various forms of pain relief, and it is not surprising that a large part of what is taught in antenatal classes involves information about this. We will continue now with a look at some of the options for pain control (analgesia) during labour.

2.5.2   Analgesia during labour

The perception of and reaction to pain is something that varies a lot between individuals. There is no doubt that all women who are conscious during childbirth experience some pain, but just how much is hard to say. Much is made in antenatal classes of using breathing rhythms to help alleviate the pain. Different breathing patterns are recommended for different stages of labour, depending on what is being achieved: an expulsive contraction (to get the baby out) requires a different pattern from a dilating contraction (to increase the aperture of the cervix). Figure 2.13 shows one example of such recommended breathing patterns. However, altering the breathing is not always sufficient to cope with the pain, and recourse to drugs or other methods can be made.

Painkilling drugs fall into several pharmacological categories, such as sedatives or narcotics, and act in different ways to relieve pain (you will learn more of this in Chapter 4). The choice of painkiller during labour depends not only on the severity of the pain, but is also tempered by the effect that the drug will have on the baby.

❑   How will the drug reach the baby?

◼   Through the blood supply, across the placenta.

If the drug dose is sufficient to affect the mother, it is likely also to affect the immature and much smaller baby, and the effects will take longer to wear off. If the baby is insufficiently alert, it may be unable to breathe or suckle properly, and this might cause problems. But it is generally felt that the beneficial effects on the mother of small amounts of pain relief probably outweigh the effects on the baby. As you will see below, not all pain relief involves drugs, so for those women for whom such techniques work, this is a preferable approach.

Sedatives

Sedatives such as Valium or Nembutal are sometimes given early on in labour to relieve anxiety. They tend to induce drowsiness; Valium may cause memory losses. These drugs can cross the placenta within a few minutes, and the sedative effect on the baby can last up to a week.

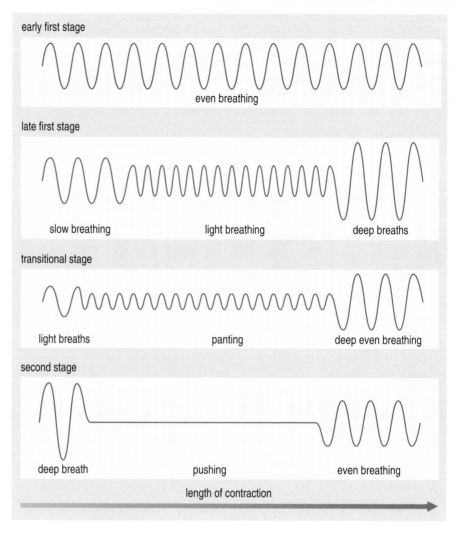

Figure 2.13 One example of breathing patterns recommended for different stages of labour.

Inhalation analgesia

This is the most widely used form of pain relief during labour. It consists of a mixture of oxygen and nitrous oxide (Entonox), or a different gas called Trilene. In the 18th and early 19th centuries, nitrous oxide was used as a recreational drug for its ability to change the state of consciousness. It can lessen the acute nature of contraction pains. It has a very short span of effectiveness, and its side-effects are mainly confined to light-headedness. It appears to have no significant effect on the baby. Inhalation analgesia is, of course, administered through a mask attached to a gas cylinder, so it can restrict mobility if the woman wants to move about. However, it is generally taken just before the peak of a contraction, when the woman is usually stationary, so this is not necessarily a problem.

Pethidine

Pethidine is a popular all-purpose painkiller. It can be given by injection, so its administration does not interfere with the woman's mobility. However, it reduces consciousness, so high doses are not compatible with trying to walk about. In common with the related drugs morphine and heroin, pethidine is addictive, although this is not a problem for a woman in labour, no matter how prolonged the experience! The main side-effect of pethidine for the mother is nausea; it also blocks the production of oxytocin.

❑   What effect might this have on labour? (Think back to Book 1, Chapter 6.)

■   It could prolong it (remember that oxytocin is involved in the contraction of smooth muscles such as those in the uterine wall).

Pethidine can cross the placenta within five minutes and can depress both respiration and suckling in the new-born baby if it is given close to the time of delivery.

Transcutaneous nervous stimulation (TENS)

TENS involves a box attached to the skin (generally on the back) which can deliver a series of mild electric shocks. It is believed that the shocks stimulate release of the body's own endorphins, which block the signals from nociceptive neurons in the same way as morphine and pethidine do (see Chapter 4). The big advantage of TENS is that the woman herself can control the frequency and strength of the electrical stimuli, thus giving her control of her own pain relief. Moreover, it does not interfere with mobility, and it does not involve injection of foreign substances into the body: the pain relief is self-generated. This sounds ideal, but unfortunately it does not appear to be effective for everybody.

Epidural anaesthesia

This involves the injection of anaesthetic directly into the spine, adjacent to the spinal cord in the lumbar region (see Figure 2.14).

❑   Thinking back to Book 2, can you say what effect this might have?

■   It would interfere with the transmission of nerve signals 'downstream' of the injection site, that is, to and from the lower abdomen and legs. This will affect both sensory and motor nerves.

Epidural anaesthesia is usually very effective as a means of pain relief, but it can cause blood pressure to drop sharply.

❑   What effect might this have?

■   The supply of oxygen to the placenta could become insufficient. Also, the woman might lose consciousness, and could even die.

Epidurals can only be administered by experienced anaesthetists who are able to resuscitate quickly women whose blood pressure drops to dangerous levels. Another drawback to epidurals is that they enforce immobility, since the woman will lose the use of her legs until the anaesthetic wears off. It is thought not to affect the fetus.

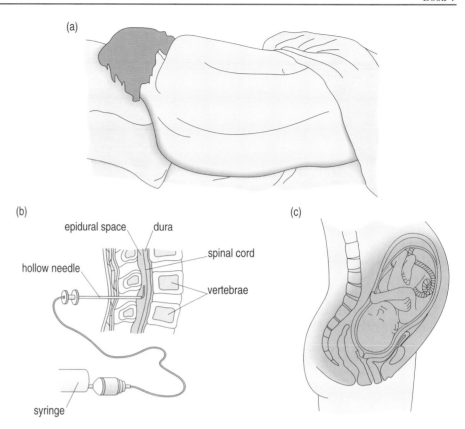

Figure 2.14 Epidural injection: (a) the position for administering the epidural; (b) position of insertion of epidural anaesthetic; (c) area affected by the epidural.

❑   Why do you think this is?

■   The drug is injected into the spine, and is largely protected from the circulation by the blood–brain barrier. Thus it is unlikely to be carried to the placenta.

Epidural anaesthesia is sometimes used when a Caesarean section is necessary: since it does not affect alertness or level of consciousness a woman can still be 'awake' for the birth of her baby.

Non-invasive methods

As you will learn in Chapter 4, the perception of pain is a very personal thing, and depends to a large extent on the psychological state of the sufferer. Women are encouraged to think of childbirth as a positive experience, and the presence of friendly faces at this time can make a big difference to how a woman copes with it. Some women like their partners to be present at the birth; others prefer a friend or a midwife. Whoever is there can help to alleviate pain by conversation, massage, and general 'tender loving care'. Back massage, in particular, often brings enormous relief. It is important for some women that the environment be 'right'; dim lights, music, continuity of care and an absence of white-coated intruders are all factors that they report as important. Some women find that hypnosis or acupuncture can relieve pain, but usually only if they have previous experience of these techniques. During labour is probably not the best time to try these methods out for the first time!

Summary of Section 2.5

1   Women react in an individual way to pregnancy; their physical and emotional feelings may be in conflict.

2   The emotional upheavals of pregnancy may mean that a couple's relationship needs to be re-negotiated.

3   Our bipedal stance means that the pelvis interferes with easy delivery, by making the hole through which the baby is expelled very small.

4   The ability to move around and the eventual delivery position can be very important for a woman's comfort and ability to deliver the baby effectively.

5   There are various ways of alleviating pain during labour. These may involve administering drugs; or stimulating the body's own painkillers; or altering the woman's state of mind.

2.6 The first few weeks after birth

After the physical and emotional ordeal of giving birth, mother and baby have to come to terms with their altered relationship. The baby must adapt to a way of life where needs are not automatically met, and where the environment can be relatively hostile. The mother must adapt to supplying the baby's needs voluntarily instead of automatically, and making the baby's environment as comfortable as possible. Both parties often have trouble with this. Physiologically, a lot has to happen around the time of birth to allow the baby to become independent of the placenta, and one or other of the newly active body systems may not function perfectly at first, although most, of course, do. From the mother's point of view, there may be great difficulty in getting over the tiredness caused by the effort of labour, and sleep will be at a premium. A new baby will need to be fed at frequent intervals, and will signal its requirements by crying. Most adults find it impossible to ignore a crying baby, and some babies seem to cry non-stop for the first few weeks of life. This can engender feelings of anger, frustration and guilt in its parents.

But this trying time can be offset by the emotions that develop between parents and their child. In the early days, this will mainly involve the mother. Much has been written about mother–baby bonding, and about the eventual strength of the bond between a mother and her child. For many people this happens automatically, but some mothers feel that they have to work hard to develop any feelings for their baby. From the baby's point of view, mother is seen first and foremost as a source of food and warmth. Only after some time will the baby recognize its mother as a special individual. As you have already learned, babies are born with certain reflexes in place, including the ability to turn towards a touch on the cheek and search for a nipple – rooting behaviour – and to suck; these reflexes ensure that the baby can feed whenever the opportunity presents itself. Let us now look at the processes involved in feeding a baby.

2.6.1 Lactation

Humans, being mammals, are able to provide their young with all the nutrients they require, and in exactly the right proportions. Until the 20th century, there was no question but that a mother would breastfeed her baby; if for some reason she was unable to do so, the baby would go to a 'wet nurse', a woman who had lost her own baby, but who still had milk. Not only does human milk supply the ideal requirements for a baby, but it also provides antibodies which will help to protect the immunologically naive baby from any pathogens it may encounter. It may, however, *transmit* some viruses, including HIV, which the mother might be carrying.

The constituents of human milk are listed in Table 2.1. These constituents vary with time: for example, the antibody supply is richest in the colostrum, the substance secreted before the 'proper' milk comes through (see below). Table 2.1 refers to what is called 'peak' or 'mature' milk, that which is produced once lactation is well established. The constituents are highly species-specific, and cows' milk is a poor substitute for human milk. The production of milk is a considerable drain on the mother's resources, and she will need extra nourishment herself throughout the period of lactation.

Lactation, the production of milk, is a very well-researched area. It all hinges on the structure of the *mammary gland*, shown in Figure 2.15.

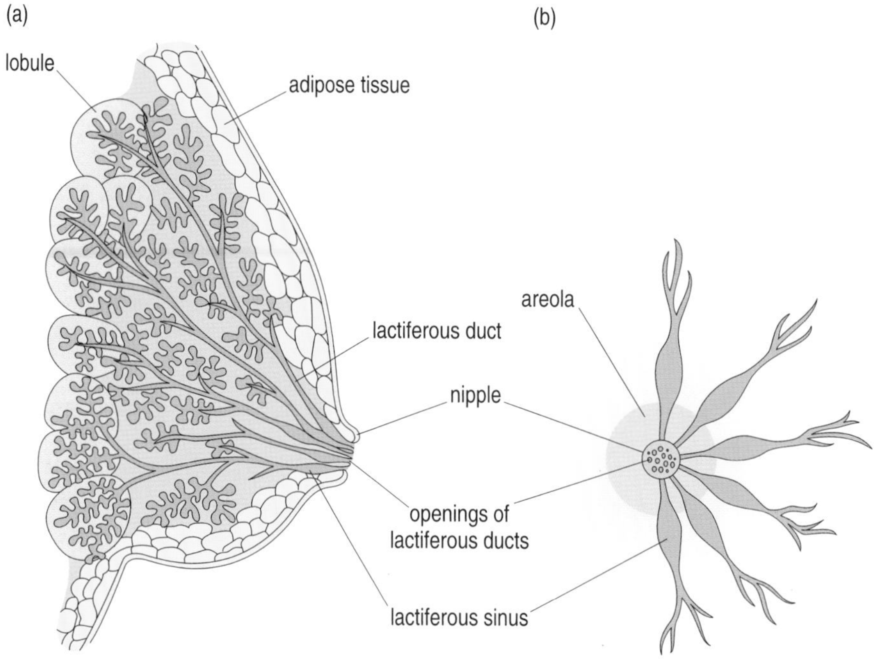

Table 2.1 Constituents of human and cows' milk. Numbers are concentrations in grams per litre.

	Human	Cow
Fat	38	37
Casein*	4	28
Other milk proteins	6	6
Lactose	65	45
Calcium	0.3	1.2

* A protein found in milk.

Figure 2.15 Structure of a mammary gland: (a) section through the right breast of a lactating woman; (b) front view of a nipple showing the openings of the lactiferous ducts.

The mammary gland is fundamentally a modified skin gland which, in embryos of both sexes, develops inwards as a tube with a few branches. There is little further development after birth in males, but in females puberty is accompanied by an increase in cell number, overall size, and branching complexity. This results in the adult pattern of glandular secretory units and ducts. The ducts converge towards the areola (the pigmented area round the nipple), and widen to form lactiferous (literally, 'milk-carrying') sinuses, which will act as milk reservoirs during lactation. This expansion depends on the increased oestrogen secretion that occurs at puberty (see above). Interestingly, the cyclic release of oestrogen in a non-pregnant woman also affects breast size, and many women find that their breasts change in size and consistency during their menstrual cycles. During pregnancy there is massive growth of the glands, in preparation for lactation. This seems to be under the influence of both oestrogen and progestogen, along with the pituitary hormone **prolactin**.

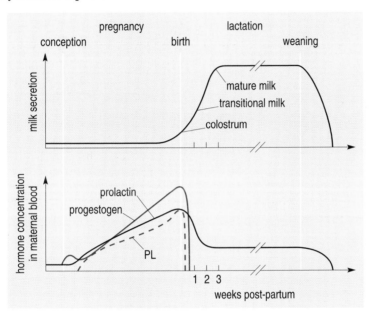

Figure 2.16   The sequence of hormone changes in the maternal circulation that underlie the onset of lactation. PL = placental lactogen.

Just as the growth of the breast itself is under hormonal control, so too is the production of milk, and prolactin plays a vital role in milk production. It is believed that a placental hormone, called placental lactogen (PL), may also play a part in this, but the evidence here is rather uncertain. Figure 2.16 shows how various hormones change through pregnancy and lactation. Progestogen and PL drop sharply at birth, but prolactin declines slowly to a plateau which is then maintained throughout the period of lactation. This, together with other evidence, suggests that there are actually two phases to lactation: initiation and maintenance. This correlates well with women's experience of the process: when the milk 'comes in', after an initial period when only colostrum is made, there may be considerable discomfort and emotional upset (indeed, this is thought to contribute to the 'baby blues' that many women experience), but once breastfeeding is established, there is usually no further trouble. The initiation is triggered by the fall in progestogen (and possibly PL), and the maintenance is controlled by the persistent level of prolactin.

❏   What does this suggest about the role of progestogen?

◼   It *inhibits* the lactation that would otherwise be stimulated by prolactin.

So much for getting the milk made, but how is it transferred to the baby? Milk is secreted at a fairly constant rate, but the baby feeds intermittently. This is where the importance of the lactiferous ducts lies: as much as 80% of the secreted milk can be stored here before a feed. Although a baby is said to feed by 'sucking', this is not strictly accurate, as in fact the baby repeatedly squeezes the nipple between its tongue and its hard palate. This sends signals to the hypothalamus, and causes the production of the hormone oxytocin from the posterior pituitary gland.

❑   What is the effect of oxytocin?

◼   Oxytocin promotes smooth muscle contraction.

At the breast, oxytocin affects tiny muscles surrounding the areola and nipple and results in the ejection of milk in a series of spurts. Observation of a feeding baby will show that for one side of the partnership at least, this is an ecstatic moment; the delight shown by the baby is an important part of the bonding mechanism between it and its mother. The mother herself can have mixed feelings about the process: some women find breastfeeding an intensely pleasurable experience, but others find it quite uncomfortable. Oxytocin can also stimulate contractions of the uterus at this time, giving so-called after-pains. The emotional dimension of breastfeeding is demonstrated if mother and baby are briefly separated: when the mother thinks about the baby, it is not unusual for milk to flow spontaneously from her breasts. The physical aspects of the oxytocin reaction are shown in Figure 2.17.

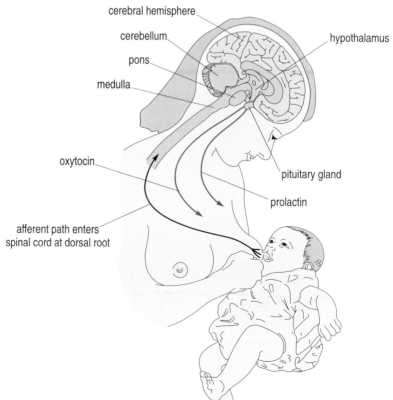

Figure 2.17   Milk ejection in a breastfeeding woman.

Some women find it impossible to breastfeed. This may be for physical reasons such as an inability to produce milk, or having very tender nipples, or for psychological reasons. Some women do not want to be or, for reasons of employment, cannot be tied down to a regular breastfeeding schedule; others simply find the whole business distasteful. For these women the option of bottle-feeding is preferred. Babies thrive on correctly reconstituted powdered milk: the main difference is that it offers no immunological protection as breast milk and colostrum do. The fashion for breast- or bottle-feeding changes at intervals, and women who choose the 'unfashionable' option are sometimes made to feel guilty about their choice. However, feeding a baby is an intensely personal experience, and is properly the business only of the family concerned.

2.6.2   Life after birth

After giving birth a woman will probably be very sore, particularly if she has tears or cuts in the perineum (the area between the urethra and the anus) that have been stitched, and she will be bleeding fairly copiously for several days. Furthermore, she will be very tired, and, if she is breastfeeding her baby, will not have the opportunity of uninterrupted sleep that she may feel she needs. The abrupt change in hormone levels that follows birth may have a profound emotional impact on her too. All in all, many women feel that they would like nothing better than to spend several days in bed after giving birth. However, there are good reasons for most women to get up and about quite soon: mobility can help to prevent constipation (which, besides being unpleasant in itself, can cause problems with a stitched or torn perineum), and also helps the postural muscles to return more quickly to their non-pregnant state. Also, financial constraints have made hospital stays shorter and shorter, and it is not unusual for women to return home the day after giving birth. In many cases there will be little opportunity to rest, as the woman is often the sole carer in the family, and may have other children to attend to as well as the new baby. Some women suffer from post-natal depression to varying extents, adding to the general burdens of motherhood. Even in the best of circumstances, new mothers universally report exhaustion for some time after birth, and, of course, this is not conducive to wanting sex. However, a partner may well have a very strong desire to resume sexual activities as soon as possible, and this can lead to tension between them. Some hospitals advise women not to engage in sex until they have been checked at six weeks after birth to ensure 'everything is back to normal'; they are often offered advice on contraception at this stage. For some women, even at this time the thought of sex is abhorrent; for others the advice comes too late and they may already be pregnant again. This again highlights the importance of treating people as individuals, each with their own desires, needs and recovery rates.

Summary of Section 2.6

1   After birth, mother and baby undergo physical, emotional and organizational changes.

2   It is usual for mother and baby to experience strong bonding with each other.

3   Much of the bonding comes about through feeding processes.

4   Human milk is ideally suited to a baby's needs, offering nutrition and immunological protection, but some viruses can be transmitted through milk.

5   Milk production and delivery is made possible by the structure of the mammary gland, a modified skin gland.

6   The production and delivery of milk is controlled by levels of several hormones.

7   Women experience great tiredness for some time after delivery; this is not conducive to early resumption of sexual activity.

2.7 Life begins at 40: the menopause

The majority of women (if they survive to their 50s) have between 30 and 40 years of reproductive life. In past years, when life expectancy was not as great as it is today, many women died while still at the height of their reproductive abilities. But nowadays it is uncommon for women to die at such a young age, and most will continue to live healthy and productive lives for many years after they have lost the ability to have children. More than a third of a woman's entire life can be spent in this post-reproductive state. The time of life when a woman's ovaries are ceasing their monthly cycles is heralded for many by the cessation of menstrual periods, or the **menopause**. The average age of onset of the menopause is around 51 years, but of course individuals differ in this. Because of this definition, 'menopause' is not a term that can be applied to men, who may be able to continue reproductive activities until they die. However, it is certainly true that men can undergo emotional turmoil associated with a similar time of life.

What biological changes in women underlie this change of life? The most fundamental cause is a gradual 'running down' of the ovaries, that actually begins about a decade before menopause itself. Ovarian failure is not due to a lack of eggs to ovulate – there are still many thousands left – but in a decline in the sensitivity of the *follicles* to stimulation by pituitary hormones. As a result, the follicles secrete less and less oestrogen. The symptoms generally associated with the menopause are due to *oestrogen deficiency*, and some medical practitioners consider the menopause to be an oestrogen deficiency disease, which can be alleviated by hormone replacement therapy (HRT). Because of the lack of oestrogen, no ovulation takes place, and so there is no corpus luteum to make progestogen. This means that there is a *secondary* hormonal deficiency too. Modern HRT regimes supply both oestrogen and progestogen.

However, the post-menopausal woman still makes some female sex hormones: they are produced not by the ovaries but by the adrenal cortex. The ovaries now synthesize testosterone instead, and some of this testosterone may be converted to an oestrogen by other tissues, notably the liver. So although the levels of female hormones are reduced, they are not entirely absent. Variations in individual levels may go some way to explaining why different women may experience different degrees of discomfort associated with the menopause.

❏   What symptoms do you associate with the menopause?

■   Hot flushes, dry and itchy skin, pain associated with sexual intercourse, an increased risk of cardiovascular disease and bone degeneration, and emotional upsets are the most commonly known ones.

How does a lack of oestrogen have these disparate effects? In many cases this is far from clear. For example, hot flushes and night sweats occur because the set-point for body temperature becomes lower: it is not known how hormone levels affect this.

❏   What effect would a lowering of the set-point have? (Think back to Book 3, Chapter 4.)

■   Even under normal conditions, the brain may perceive the body to be too hot, and will trigger a sweating response to rectify this.

However, other symptoms can more easily be shown to be related to oestrogen levels. Dry and itchy skin, and the general 'sagging' that some women experience, happen because low oestrogen levels favour the disintegration of collagen and elastin fibres in the skin and elsewhere, leading to a loss of tone. Underlying muscles also tend to shrink.

❏   What other effect will this have on the skin? (Think back to Book 1, Chapter 3.)

■   Wrinkles.

The itchiness is due to deterioration of nerve endings in the skin, which can be perceived as an itchy sensation, at its worst a feeling of ants crawling on the skin (called *formication*). About 20% of menopausal women suffer from this.

A common complaint of menopausal women is pain during intercourse. As oestrogen levels drop, muscles in the walls of the uterus and vagina become replaced with fibrous tissue, and the organs shrivel (although the vagina remains able to accommodate a penis). The vaginal epithelium also changes, and secretions become much less. The dryness that this causes can result in discomfort; also, because the vaginal pH changes, it is no longer acidic enough to protect against pathogens. Minor infections, and consequent pain, may occur. Bone degeneration and osteoporosis are also known to be the result of an oestrogen-dependent change, this time in the balance between the cycle of synthesis and degradation that characterize healthy bone (see Book 2, Chapter 2). Mineral deposits in the bone become lessened, and bones gradually become brittle and prone to fractures. This can be minimized by the inclusion of more calcium in the diet, along with vitamin D to facilitate its uptake from the gut (see Book 3, Chapter 3).

The different incidence of cardiovascular disease between men and pre-menopausal women has been shown to be due to the protective effects of oestrogen (see Book 3, Chapter 2). Thus it is not unexpected that as oestrogen levels decline, the risk of heart disease in women increases until it matches the 'male' level (see Figure 2.18). It does not, however, surpass this level, and a woman who is of normal weight, a non-smoker, and who exercises adequately is not at any *particular* risk.

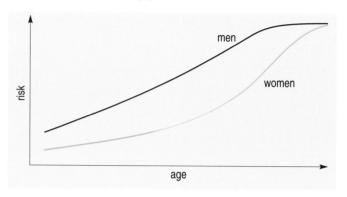

Figure 2.18   Age-specific deaths from coronary heart disease in men and women.

Perhaps the most difficult symptoms to explain precisely in terms of oestrogen deficiency are the emotional ones. There is no doubt that in the developed world, where youth and sexual activity are highly prized, it can be most distressing for women to find evidence of their bodies' ageing, and this commonly leads to some degree of depression. But this is certainly not the case in some other cultures. In many countries where the 'youth culture' is not so prevalent, older women are highly valued for their acquired wisdom and experience. And it is interesting that in these societies the menopause is not associated with all the problems that we discussed above; on the contrary, it may be welcomed as a badge of honour. This suggests that notwithstanding the reductionist explanation of oestrogen deficiency as a cause of women's woes, there is a large psychological component which affects how women deal with the physiological change of life.

Summary of Section 2.7

1   The menopause marks the end of a woman's reproductive life, with the cessation of menstrual periods.

2   Symptoms associated with menopause in the developed world are both physical and emotional.

3   Many of the physical symptoms can be explained by oestrogen deficiency.

4   Many of the emotional symptoms can be explained by cultural conditioning.

2.8 Conclusions

This chapter has looked at some of the facets of reproductive life. Many of the items described, such as changes at puberty, apply to everybody, whether or not they are actively reproducing; others, such as lactation, apply only to some members of society. But reproduction affects us all: as one commentator puts it, 'From a purely biological viewpoint, the "purpose" of life is to generate more life' (Mepham, 1987, pp. 9–10). In this course we have tried not to be restricted by such a narrow approach, and here, although we have talked about the part played by, for example, hormones in our reproductive processes, we have also tried to emphasize the emotional and social constraints that we have collectively placed on this most fundamental of behaviours.

Objectives for Chapter 2

After reading this chapter, you should be able to:

2.1 Define and use, or recognize definitions and applications of, each of the words printed in **bold** in the text.

2.2 Describe the structure of the Y chromosome and suggest how it might have evolved. (*Question 2.1*)

2.3 Describe with diagrams the development of the external genitals. (*Question 2.3*)

2.4 Discuss the physical and emotional changes that occur at puberty. (*Question 2.2*)

2.5 Discuss the importance of rites of passage and learning courtship behaviour. (*Question 2.4*)

2.6 Outline the role of hormones in sexual behaviour. (*Question 2.5*)

2.7 Describe the main forms of analgesia available for labour. (*Question 2.6*)

2.8 Describe the development of the mammary gland from the embryonic stages to lactation. (*Question 2.3*)

2.9 Describe how physical changes lead to the symptoms associated with the menopause. (*Question 2.7*)

Questions for Chapter 2

Question 2.1 (*Objective 2.2*)

How does the Y chromosome pair with the X chromosome at meiosis?

Question 2.2 (*Objective 2.4*)

List four secondary sexual characteristics. Which do you think would affect the emotional process of growing up?

Question 2.3 (*Objective 2.3 and 2.8*)

Which hormones are involved in the development of (a) the genitals, (b) the mammary glands?

Question 2.4 (*Objective 2.5*)

Why have societies developed complex rules surrounding sexual behaviour?

Question 2.5 (*Objective 2.6*)

Do sex hormones affect behaviour?

Question 2.6 (*Objective 2.7*)

What factors need to be considered when deciding upon pain relief during labour?

Question 2.7 (*Objective 2.9*)

List three common symptoms of menopause, and give a reductionist explanation for each of them.

References

Gordon, R. (1993) *The Alarming History of Medicine*, Mandarin, London.

Mepham, T. B. (1987) *Physiology of Lactation*, Open University Press, Milton Keynes.

Stoppard, M. (1986) *The Pregnancy and Birth Handbook*, Dorling Kindersley, London.

CHAPTER 3
HUMAN SEXUALITY

3.1 Introduction

The previous chapter discussed sexual behaviour but did not look in detail at the underlying behavioural processes; this is the topic of the present chapter. Sexual behaviour illustrates the complexity and richness of human behaviour and the necessity for holistic explanations for what people think and do. People are said to have **sexual motivation**, i.e. a tendency to be 'moved' voluntarily to engage in sexual behaviour. (The terms 'sexual arousal' and 'sex drive' can also be used to describe the state of the central nervous system that underlies sexual behaviour.) A moment's reflection will reveal the multitude of factors that are involved in trying to explain such motivation and how this can get translated into sexual behaviour. Thus the present chapter will be as much about the psychology of human sexuality as about its physiology.

List some of the factors that are involved in sexual behaviour, reflecting upon the extent to which they might be purely human ones or ones shared with other animals.

At a certain basic level there would appear to be something in common between many animal species, e.g. the role of hormones and the presence of an opposite-sex partner in arousing sexual motivation. However, in humans there are additional factors involved. These include such things as attempting to enhance our self-image and to improve the image that we suppose a desired person holds of us. Sexual behaviour can be motivated by a conscious intention to sustain or consolidate a relationship. Humans might be persuaded to engage in sex because of peer pressure. In addition, for many people, fantasy and imagination are important determinants of sexual motivation – such 'higher-order' processes are not a feature of the sexuality of other animal species! And of course, for many sexual relationships, something peculiar to humans that we call 'love' is a crucial context. Conversely, sexual behaviour might be *resisted* for a variety of religious and cultural taboos.

Any attempt to provide a full explanation of sexual behaviour will need to be holistic, calling upon information at various levels of analysis. No one discipline, whether sociology, psychology or biology, can claim to give a full account. Such a variety of factors that act both to promote and to inhibit sexual behaviour make it difficult to produce all-embracing theories.

As a tentative start, it might be suggested that in both men and women, sexual motivation arises from a complex interaction between several factors, as represented in Figure 3.1. Of course, you might feel that the richness of human sexual experience cannot be reduced to a series of boxes and arrows. You would be right, and such a thought reminds us of the complex nature of human behaviour and motivation. However, in trying to achieve a scientific understanding of sexual behaviour, as well as acknowledging the holistic aspects, we need to construct some rigorous theories and models. These are bound to use reductionist terms.

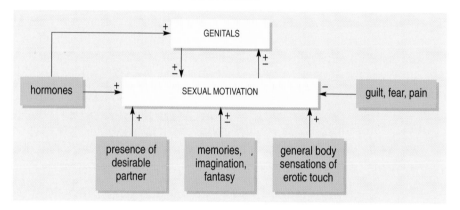

Figure 3.1 Representation of the factors that contribute to sexual motivation. Arrows pointing into the box labelled 'sexual motivation' represent factors that contribute to this. A negative sign means that the factor inhibits motivation, a plus sign that it excites motivation. A combination of both a plus and a minus represents the possibility of either excitation or inhibition, depending upon circumstances. The arrow leaving 'sexual motivation' represents the influence of motivation on the state of the genitals.

Suppose there is a desired person, whose presence activates those nervous system processes that underlie sexual motivation. Who constitutes such a desired person will itself be influenced by early experiences. There will be memories and fantasies, fueled perhaps by such things as erotic films and books. There is also the possibility of negative influences upon motivation arising from, say, fear or guilt. Hormones play a role in sensitizing motivational processes. Note the reciprocal interactions between 'sexual motivation' – a central nervous system (CNS) process – and the genitals; these interactions are mediated via the peripheral nervous system. Stimulation from the genitals can increase motivation, if pleasant, or decrease it, if the sensation is unpleasant – hence the plus and minus signs in Figure 3.1. Reciprocally, the motivational processes serve to change the state of the genitals, e.g. engorgement of the vagina with blood or erection of the penis. The minus sign represents the possibility of inhibition of genital arousal by signals arising from the CNS. These changes will in turn change the nature of the feedback signal to the central motivational processes. Hormones exerting both central effects and effects at the genitals are produced by the testes, ovaries and adrenal glands.

How does this complex interactive system come into being? The next section looks at the developmental factors involved.

Summary of Section 3.1

1   Human sexual behaviour and the processes that underlie it have much in common with those of non-humans. However, in addition there are peculiarly human cognitive factors such as self-image and religious and cultural taboos. Imagination and emotion are also involved.

2   There exist reciprocal relationships between the central state of sexual motivation and the state of arousal of the genitals.

3.2 Developmental factors

Book 3, Chapter 6, looked at some of the early developmental factors that play a role in the determination of feeding motivation and behaviour. A similar set of considerations applies to sexual motivation.

First, there is the genome, the set of genes we all inherit from our parents and which set a direction for our subsequent physiological development (discussed in Chapter 2). The genome and its physiological environment (e.g. hormones) interact to determine the course of development. Later there will be a social environment which also plays a role. (See Figure 3.2.) Memories of early social context will be significant later in helping to influence the direction that sexual motivation will take. Thus, there arises a nervous system constructed in a way that normally leads later to sexual motivation directed towards a partner having particular characteristics. As part of this process, the nervous system forms representations of ideal forms of sexual partner and these play a role in fantasies and motivation directed towards others. If development takes an abnormal course, as a result of aberrant hormonal or social context, the adult nervous system might be incapable of responding sexually or only respond in bizarre ways.

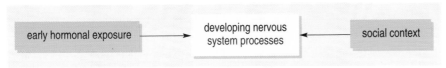

Figure 3.2   Factors influencing the development of sexuality.

Before birth and shortly afterwards, the presence of hormones biases the direction that sexual development takes (Chapter 2). For example, hormones play a role in establishing the structure of the CNS processes that underlie later sexual motivation and behaviour. One such structure that figures prominently in accounts of this process is the so-called *pre-optic area* of the hypothalamus (Tobet and Fox, 1992), which is different in men compared to women. The social environment (e.g. maternal behaviour) also plays a role, interacting in complex ways with early hormonal influences to determine later sexuality. One can appreciate that during this period of growth and development, there must be complex interactions occurring between neural structure and environment. As discussed in Chapter 2, there will also be different reactions towards the growing child, depending upon its possession of male or female genitals.

Certain hormonal effects on development – in the present context, those of testosterone – have been generally thought to occur only at a particular stage (before, and just after, birth). The period during which the brain is susceptible to these effects is known as the **critical period**. The action of hormones at this stage is termed an **organizing effect**, meaning that they serve to organize the neural structures that will later play a role in sexual motivation and behaviour. More recent evidence suggests that the critical period is not quite as absolute as was once thought; hormones can continue to exert some organizing effect even into adulthood.

During fetal life and shortly after birth, rates of secretion of GnRH, FSH, LH and other reproductive hormones (described in Chapter 2) are high and some of these exert an organizing effect on the structures involved in sexuality. The hormones present following sexual maturity act upon these organized neural structures to sensitize them in a way that contributes to sexual motivation and behaviour, termed an **activational effect**. An activational effect is one that is more or less reversible by a change (up or down) in the level of the hormone responsible for the effect, and is relatively independent of age. In contrast, organizing effects are irreversible and occur mainly during a limited time-frame of early development (Beatty, 1992).

One important feature that only humans might be supposed to possess is the concept of gender identity (see Chapter 2). At some time between two and four years of age a child normally acquires the concept 'I am a girl' or 'I am a boy' – a dichotomous classification process (Bancroft, 1989). After the child has formed this central organizing concept, events in the world, reactions and inner feelings can be construed in terms of the concept. Formation of such a concept depends in part upon hormonal and social influences, but presumably once acquired will be able to organize to some extent the interpretation to be placed upon sexually related experiences and sources of information.

Following early development, the sex hormones are inactive until puberty. Puberty marks a second phase of hormonal input on sexual development, from the sex hormones produced by the gonads.

❑   What are these hormonal effects?

■   Amongst other things, breasts enlarge in girls and the voice breaks in boys.

This gives a further opportunity for complex hormone–environment interactions to occur, as the pressures to conform to either sex role can be accentuated (see Chapter 2).

Testosterone is sometimes thought of as 'the male sex hormone'. However, as you learnt in Chapter 2, it is also found in the bloodstream in women, being produced by both the ovaries and the adrenal glands. Androgens other than testosterone (i.e. others of the so-called male hormones) are also found in women. Sex drive in women, as in men, shows an androgen dependence.

Later in the chapter we return to the discussion of sex hormones in the context of motivation and sexual behaviour, where their role will be interpreted in terms of the whole system.

Summary of Section 3.2

1   The genome exerts an influence in interaction with the internal and external environments to determine the processes underlying sexual behaviour.

2   During the critical period, hormones exert an organizing effect on the neural structures involved in sexuality; in adults, hormones exert a mainly activational effect on these structures.

3   Although the process of human development has much in common with that of other animals, there are some peculiarly human features of development that apply to sexuality, such as the notion of our gender identity and how others react towards this identity.

3.3 Sexual motivation

3.3.1 Introduction

What constitutes the biological basis of sexual motivation and its satiety, is a fascinating topic that has invited speculation throughout history. Current scientific opinion would see sexual motivation as a property of the CNS, which is influenced by hormones secreted outside of it. The following sections explore the evidence in men and women.

3.3.2 Sexual motivation in men

Testosterone plays a crucial role in maintaining human sexual motivation. By analogy with the results obtained in non-human experimental subjects, it is assumed that androgens affect the brain, to sensitize certain key neural centres that underlie sexual motivation (Everitt and Bancroft, 1991).

In men, androgens, especially testosterone, seem to be necessary (though not sufficient) for the arousal of sexual desire. Most men show a slowly decreasing sexual function with advancing years which corresponds to a reduction in testosterone secretion with age, as shown in Figure 3.3. However, individual variation is large and it would probably be wrong to see the decline in testosterone level as being the sole underlying factor in reduced desire.

Total loss of androgens in men is followed by a reduction in, and then loss of, sexual arousal, as indexed by self-reports of the frequency of sexual thoughts and their associated arousal value. Following castration (removal of testes, e.g. due to testicular cancer), androgen level falls rapidly in a matter of hours and yet sexual activity can persist for weeks or even (in

Figure 3.3 The approximate relationship between rate of testosterone secretion and age in men.

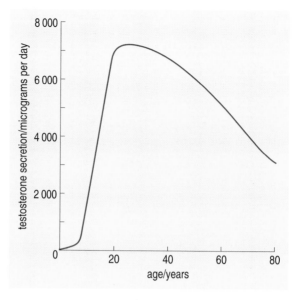

some anecdotal cases) months or years. In one survey, two-thirds of the subjects investigated had lost all sexual motivation and activity within one year of the operation. However, some individuals were still functioning sexually 10 years after the operation. To some extent, androgens of adrenal origin might be able to substitute for the lost testicular source. Another factor in maintaining motivation is thought to be the subject's previous experience, cognitions and expectations about sexual behaviour. In cases where loss of sexual interest is due to a reduction in androgen levels, androgen replacement restores the frequency and the quality of the subject's erotic thoughts.

❑   What is the hormonal (androgen-induced) effect just described? Recall the two classes of hormonal effects discussed in Section 3.2. What is the important difference between these effects?

■   The effect just described is an activational effect; it is reversible. In contrast, the organizing effects of hormones are irreversible.

Strangely, even males without androgen can maintain an erection in response to certain visual erotic stimuli, which might explain the cases of persistence. Erectile failure might be a complex function of, amongst other things, the male's perception of the loss of desire. In cases where sexual activity persists, there might be use of appropriate visual stimuli. Some castrated men, or those with a very low androgen-producing capacity, seem to have fairly normal sexual lives. However, they often have relatively low levels of sexual desire. In such cases, a successful sexual relationship may rely upon having a partner who is happy to initiate sexual activity, for this can reduce the psychological pressure on the male.

The so-called *anti-androgens* are artificial substances that compete with androgens at their target sites but do not have the excitatory effects that androgens have. They could be described as androgen antagonists (Book 2, Chapter 3). In experiments with rats, the effect of injections of anti-androgens depended upon the animal's prior experience. In sexually naive rats, sexual motivation was suppressed, but sexually experienced rats showed no such reduction in motivation. In some cases, men have been treated with anti-androgens for sexual deviation and hypersexuality (i.e. excessive and troublesome sex drive). For these individuals, there was a loss of libido and a reduction in capacity to achieve an erection, followed by a loss of the ability to reach orgasm. Thus the change was only in the intensity of sexual motivation, not in its direction.

So much for some of the factors that switch on sexual motivation but what serves to switch it off? What causes the sexual satiation which follows orgasm? Loss of motivation is not caused by a simple reversal of the hormonal state that played a role in its arousal. Thus the sudden onset of sexual exhaustion at orgasm is not caused by a sharp drop in the level of testosterone in the body. Neither is it caused by a loss of seminal fluids. There is no evidence that the reduction in seminal pressure which occurs at orgasm switches off motivation. Rather, by extrapolation from evidence obtained from experiments on rats, it would seem that the neural events that underlie orgasm have two effects. One is the intense arousal and pleasure, but this is followed by a process of active inhibition of the sexual motivation processes, thereby preventing further arousal (Rodriguez-Manzo and Fernandez-Guasti, 1994). See Figure 3.4.

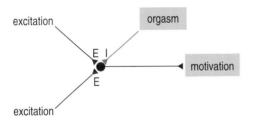

Figure 3.4   Representation of the possible process underlying sexual satiation. There are various neural influences on sexual motivation, represented by excitatory synapses (E) and an inhibitory synapse (I). Activity arises in the inhibitory neuron as a result of orgasm.

Look at Figure 3.4 and work out how, based upon this scheme, a revival of sexual motivation might be induced artificially.

Since activity in the neural processes underlying sexual motivation is actively inhibited immediately following orgasm, this suggests that a revival might be induced by an antagonist to the transmitter employed by the inhibitory neurons involved. Injection of the drug yohimbine (an antagonist to adrenergic receptors) into male rats is followed by revival of sexual motivation and copulatory ability. Interestingly, yohimbine, obtained from the bark of the yohimbine tree, has commonly been used as an aphrodisiac by men and has been claimed by some practitioners to be useful in the treatment of **erectile dysfunction** (failure to maintain a state of erection). However, the results are sometimes disappointing.

3.3.3 Sexual motivation in women

One might have supposed that whereas male sexual motivation is largely under the control of testosterone, the hormonal contribution to sexual motivation in females would be mainly oestrogen. Neurons with receptors for oestrogen are found in various brain regions (e.g. amygdala, septum and hypothalamus) and oestrogen is known to be able to change the firing patterns of neurons in the hypothalamus of females (Sherwin, 1991). Thus oestrogen can affect brain regions known to be involved in emotion and sexual motivation.

However, there is some (though not conclusive) evidence to suggest that androgens play the principal role in female sexual motivation, as in males. These are secreted from the adrenal glands in both men and women. Anti-androgens given as a treatment for acne are reported to lower sexual motivation in women as well as in men (Bancroft, 1989). Hence one might be able to explain, at least in part, how sexual motivation survives menopause when oestrogen levels are sharply reduced. In women receiving supplementary androgen at this time, sexuality is reported to improve. Comparing women of different ages and in different hormonal states, a positive correlation has been observed between (1) blood testosterone levels and (2) vaginal lubrication and breast sensations (Myers and Morokoff, 1986). This suggests a central role of testosterone in sexual arousal in women as well as men.

There are conflicting reports of whether sexual motivation fluctuates with the changes in blood levels of oestrogen which accompany the menstrual cycle. Some reports suggest little or no fluctuation of motivation over the cycle (Myers and Morokoff, 1986). However, in a study of several thousand women reported by Bancroft (1989), sexual interest oscillated in phase with the woman's own reported feeling of general well-being. This suggests a non-specific role of mood, rather than a more specific effect of oestrogen, on sexual motivation. It is possible that a contribution to such fluctuations in sexual interest might also arise from the woman's knowledge of her current biological state regarding the possibility of pregnancy. For example, anxiety about the risk of pregnancy might reduce sexual motivation; but in some women, the 'thrill' associated with this risk might *increase* motivation. This underlies the fact that sexuality needs to be understood in terms of its context.

Comparing female sexual arousal with that of the male, in many cases the female capacity for repeated orgasm is considerably greater than that of the male, suggesting that the inhibition of arousal which follows orgasm may be slower to take effect in some females (Figure 3.4).

The following section looks at the response of the body to sexual arousal, which can be understood within the context of an interacting system of the kind shown in Figure 3.1.

Summary of Section 3.3

1   In both men and women, androgens play a role in maintaining sexual motivation and erotic thoughts; this is an activational effect.

2   In both sexes, loss of androgens can be followed by a loss of motivation.

3   The loss of sexual motivation at orgasm would appear to be due to exertion of inhibition within the CNS.

4   If a similar inhibitory process can play a role in both male and female sexual motivation, then it would appear to be less strongly activated by orgasm in many women.

3.4 The sexual response

3.4.1 Introduction

Section 3.4 will focus upon the changes that are seen at the genitals at the time of sexual arousal. Within this chapter, a division into sections on sexual motivation and sexual response is merely a matter of organizational convenience, since the response will depend upon the central motivation and the central state will in turn be a function of the peripheral (i.e. genital) response as transmitted to the brain via the tactile and visual senses. This is represented in Figure 3.1. The penis and the vagina are highly vascularized organs; in other words, they contain many blood vessels. In the normal state of these organs their blood vessels are relatively empty. Erection of the penis and clitoris is brought about by their filling with blood.

Although the focus of Section 3.4 is upon events at the genitals, it should be noted that there are changes that occur throughout the body accompanying sexual arousal and behaviour. For example, blood flow to the skin increases due to surface vasodilation. Heart rate greatly increases between the resting state and orgasm. Such an elevation in heart rate is something that a person recovering from heart problems might need to take into consideration when resuming sexual relations. Following a heart attack, a programme of *gradual* sexual rehabilitation might usefully be devised (Bancroft, 1989). This topic is a reminder of the fact that healthy sexuality can be best built upon a general state of good health.

3.4.2 The sexual response in men

Normal function

The small arteries that supply blood to the penis are normally constricted and this accounts for its flaccid form. Sexual excitement is associated with a dilation of these small arteries, their state being determined by the tension of the smooth muscle in their walls. (See Figure 3.5.) Note the greater ease of blood inflow (wider arteries) accompanied by a greater resistance to outflow (narrower veins) in the erect state. Note also the enlargement of the blood-filled spaces (sinusoids) within the penis, that occurs with erection.

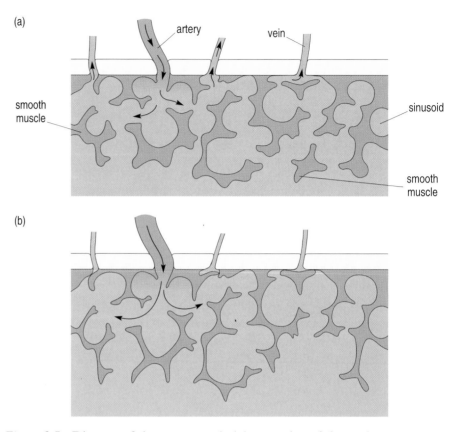

Figure 3.5   Diagram of the process underlying erection of the penis: (a) flaccid state; (b) erect state. Note the enlargement of the blood-filled spaces (sinusoids) in (b).

The state of the smooth muscle in the blood vessel and sinusoid walls is in turn determined by the activity of sympathetic and parasympathetic nerves that supply the muscle. The normal flaccid state is maintained by a background level (termed 'tone') of activity of the smooth muscles caused by activity in sympathetic nerves. Corresponding to sexual excitation, stimulation of parasympathetic neurons and inhibition of the sympathetic neurons that innervate the penis results in muscular relaxation and thereby dilation of the small arteries and sinusoids (Bancroft, 1989).

The determinants of the activity of these neurons are both local and central, i.e. instigated in the brain. (See Figure 3.6.) The combination of local and central events determines the state of penile erection. Highly sensitive mechanoreceptors (a type of receptor that respond to changes in pressure) located in the penis itself (especially towards the end) are activated by tactile stimulation. The afferent neurons whose tips these mechanoreceptors form (e.g. neuron 1) connect to interneurons in the spinal cord, e.g. neuron 2 and then neuron 3. Neuron 3 then makes contact with parasympathetic neuron 4.

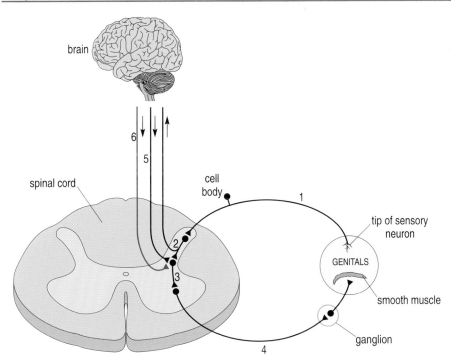

Figure 3.6   Possible representation of some of the neurons involved in the parasympathetic contribution to erection. (A similar model can probably also be adapted to apply to clitoral erection in women.)

The activity of neurons such as neuron 4 determines the state of relaxation of smooth muscle in the wall of a small artery. Neuron 4 is under the control of both local and central factors, via neuron 3. Neuron 3 is excited by descending influences from the brain via the spinal cord (neuron 5). Neuron 1 also sends a signal to the brain (via neuron 2), which can increase central arousal. Speculatively, neuron 5 can also amplify the local effect of genital stimulation, as shown by the synaptic link to neuron 3 – for example, as activated by an erotic thought. Neuron 6, descending from the brain, exerts inhibition upon neuron 3.

Activity in the descending pathways (neurons 5 and 6) depends upon a variety of what might be termed cognitive factors. These include, on the excitatory side (via neuron 5), the attractiveness of the partner, a feeling of engagement with the sexual union and a perception of the success of the whole procedure and, on the inhibitory side (via neuron 6), anxiety or perhaps guilt. Thus, for example, the conscious recognition of erectile failure can result in a vicious circle effect that removes the necessary parasympathetic activity.

In addition to causing erection, parasympathetic impulses stimulate the mucus-secreting glands of the penis (There is a similar effect on the female genitals too.) This secretion of mucus occurs both before and during intercourse and helps in lubrication.

The term 'ejaculation' refers to the discharge of seminal fluid from the penis as a result of muscular contractions. The organization of the control of ejaculation is similar in some ways to that of erection. A combination of afferent information from tactile stimulation and descending influences from the brain triggers the reflex. However, ejaculation involves activation of sympathetic nerves. Problems with ejaculation – either its occurrence prematurely or a complete failure to occur – can be the result of inappropriate descending information from the brain. As noted in Section 3.3.2, orgasm is followed by a refractory period during which the male cannot be stimulated further; the length of this period varies with age, amongst other factors. Orgasm is accompanied by a return of the neural inputs to the small smooth muscles of the penis to those of the unaroused state and a return of the blood vessels in the penis to their unstimulated state.

Treatment with agents that affect the nervous system can alter sexual functioning and feelings. For example, serotonin reuptake inhibitors (Book 2, Chapter 3), e.g. Anafranil (clomipramine hydrochloride), a drug prescribed for obsessional neurosis and depression, often cause failure to achieve orgasm. However, the plus side of a drug such as Anafranil in the present context is that it can be used to treat premature ejaculation. As well as blocking serotonin reuptake, Anafranil appears to inhibit the peripheral adrenergic receptors of the sympathetic nervous system. When the patient is taken off Anafranil the problem of premature ejaculation commonly returns. Such drug therapy should not be seen as a panacea; there might well be relationship difficulties such as unresolved marital conflict that underlie the problem and which might be usefully addressed by counselling. In other words, there might be a need to take an holistic approach, rather than simply relying upon a chemical treatment of symptoms.

'Erectile dysfunction' is generally preferred to the lay expression of 'impotence', since the latter is often felt to have a pejorative tone. An analogous condition in women is a failure to achieve vaginal engorgement with blood and associated clitoral erection, arising from, say, a lack of interest in her partner, or anxiety. Of men attending a clinic for sexual disorders in Edinburgh, erectile dysfunction was by far the most common problem (Bancroft, 1989). There are several possible causes. They include damage to neurons in the nerve pathways just described. A failure on the part of the descending pathway to promote appropriate excitatory influences is sometimes termed a 'psychological' or 'psychogenic' cause. A full understanding of erectile dysfunction would need consideration of not only the physiology of the erectile process but also the nature of the subject's relationship. There might be conflict or other problems that need to be addressed. Thus treatment can sometimes usefully involve the partner, though some men are reluctant to agree to this.

There is the interesting question of whether androgens sensitize local neurons whose activity determines the erectile process. For example, the relationship between the decline in androgen levels with ageing and loss of erectile capacity might be mediated locally. In non-humans, such an androgen dependence of the neurons involved in the erectile process is seen. However, there is little evidence to suggest that this androgen dependence occurs in men. There is little difference in testosterone levels, between groups of men with and without erectile problems. Rather, as indicated earlier, the effect of androgens is a central one, targeting motivational processes in the brain. Thus, erectile dysfunction is unlikely to respond to supplementary androgen unless it is caused by a low sexual interest; in such cases, there *is* some evidence of benefit.

The maintenance of erection requires an adequate blood supply to the penis. Erectile dysfunction can be caused by abnormalities of the circulation rather than being a dysfunction within the neural controls on the system. There can be local atherosclerosis (Book 3, Chapter 2), i.e. occlusion of arteries within the penis, so limiting blood flow into the organ. Such a local effect might prove to be the first sign of a more general circulatory problem, as the penile arteries seem to be particularly susceptible (Bancroft, 1989). Such patients are recommended to follow the general advice concerning atherosclerosis, in terms of diet (low saturated fat content), taking exercise, avoidance of excess alcohol, and not smoking. Nicotine has an alpha adrenergic action. In other words, this drug binds to the so-called alpha adrenergic receptors, thereby mimicking the effects of adrenalin and noradrenalin in causing vasoconstriction. Therefore smoking can cause constriction of the small arteries of the penis, thus impairing the capacity for erection. What is termed **neurogenic erectile dysfunction** arises from specific dysfunction (e.g. lesions) in particular regions of the nervous system underlying the erectile process. This can be in the brain, spinal cord or peripheral nerves. Diabetes mellitus (a failure of insulin secretion – Book 3, Chapter 4) is responsible for a large percentage of cases of peripheral nerve damage.

A popular dichotomy in explaining erectile dysfunction is in terms of *either* an **organic cause** (e.g. circulatory problems such as blocked arteries) *or* a **psychogenic cause** (e.g. anxiety about sexual performance or about other aspects of life). However, as you should already have suspected from the study of SK220, this dichotomy can be too neat and simple. Whereas it might be possible to attribute *initial* causation to either source, once the problem has started then multiple factors can play a role.

Look back at Figure 3.1. Can you see the logic for the statement just made?

Suppose that the original cause is organic, e.g. the result of atherosclerosis at the penis. The resulting anxiety as a result of slight erectile dysfunction might then set up a vicious circle of effects. Overactivity of the sympathetic nervous system accompanying anxiety and stress can cause vasoconstriction in the arteries of the penis. Stress is associated with increased levels of circulating adrenalin and noradrenalin (discussed in Chapter 5 of this book) and this too has a vasoconstrictive effect at the penis.

A low testosterone level can be implicated in erectile dysfunction and in some cases supplementary androgen can prove beneficial. This might seem to be a clear case of an organic factor. However, as discussed earlier, testosterone sensitizes neurons in the CNS. Whether we would view such artificial sensitization as a recovery from organic impairment is a matter of definition and of hair-splitting philosophical debate. Also, there is some evidence that testosterone secretion is itself increased by sexual activity. Therefore a low level of testosterone might be due to an initial psychogenic cause, associated with a low level of sexual activity. Stress and depression can lower testosterone levels. Sometimes testosterone level increases following recovery of erectile function, which suggests that a psychological factor may be involved.

In spite of such evidence for complex interactions, as recently as 1990, Buvat *et al.* were able to write of erectile dysfunction (ED):

> *There continue to be two irreconcilable groups of therapists dealing with ED, the 'organic' group, including physicians and particularly surgeons, who think of erectile function only in hydraulic terms, who take even the most minor physical abnormality in a diagnostic test as evidence of 'organic' causation, and who assume that in most other cases there is a concealed physical cause waiting to be identified. Their clinical approach is preoccupied with establishing indications for surgical treatment. The 'psychogenic group', on the other hand, see symbolic somatic manifestations of psychic conflicts in every organic disease and deny any primary organic aetiology in ED.*

The approach adopted here would, of course, wish to qualify carefully the validity of any such dichotomy and make much of it a grey area rather than implying a black and white distinction.

One test that has been widely used in an attempt to distinguish cases of erectile dysfuction with an organic cause is to measure **penile tumescence** (swelling) by means of the nocturnal penile tumescence (NPT) test. The rationale for this test is based on the observation that sexually mature males generally experience three or four erections each night, corresponding to the rapid eye movement (REM) phase of sleep (discussed in Chapter 6). It was once believed that this erectile reaction circumvents any psychological problems and reveals the simple organic capacity of the local process. If there is erectile dysfunction but a normal reaction in the NPT test, then this strongly suggests lack of organic impairment and that the dysfunction is most probably associated with psychological causes. In patients with organic impairment there is a disruption of NPT (Bancroft, 1989). However, when the NPT test is abnormal, the diagnosis is less clear, since it might reflect a local abnormality (e.g. in the penile blood vessels) or might be due to a central effect associated with depression or a deficiency of hormones.

3.4.3 The sexual response in women

In women, the bodily manifestations of sexual arousal include erection of the nipples and clitoris. The erectile tissue of the clitoris is analogous to that of the male penis and its state is also under the control of the parasympathetic nervous system, which causes dilation of the small arteries supplying it with blood. In sexual arousal, the vaginal epithelium is engorged with blood and, also under the control of parasympathetic nerves, secretes a lubricating fluid. An instrument termed the vaginal photoplethysmograph permits the measurement of sexual arousal. It consists of a probe which is inserted into the vagina and which measures vaginal engorgement. In response to viewing an erotic film, there is typically an increased level of vaginal engorgement. A measure of vaginal engorgement is considered to be the best index of female sexual arousal, since it correlates rather closely with the woman's own, subjective, report of sexual arousal (Hoon, Wincze and Hoon, 1976). Furthermore, carefully controlled studies have ruled out that it is a measure of just any form of strong arousal. By contrast, the changes in the properties of the skin surface that are observed with sexual arousal also occur with surprise and novelty experienced in a *non*-sexual context.

Female orgasm, analogous to the process underlying male ejaculation, is observed as a series of rhythmic contractions of the muscles of the vagina and uterus.

❏ Could there be any biological function of female orgasm?

◼ It is possible that it might assist fertilization by helping to promote the movement of sperm into the uterus and thence into the Fallopian tubes (where fertilization may take place). The intense pleasure presumably serves as a positive reinforcer, i.e. encourages the female to engage more often in intercourse, with a corresponding potential increase in the probability of fertilization.

As in males, female arousal and orgasm are the result of a combination of local afferent information arising from the genital region and descending influences from the brain. Thus important features of Figure 3.6 apply to women.

Orgasm is commonly followed by a state of calm accompanied by a fairly rapid loss of the various indices of arousal. For example, the elevated heart rate returns to its resting level and the vaginal engorgement subsides. However, some authors dispute whether a refractory period, a post-orgasm loss of sensitivity like that of men, really exists at all in women. Attempts at accurate measurement made under laboratory conditions might not reflect the natural situation (Bancroft, 1989). However, it does appear that a woman has a higher capacity for multiple orgasm than a man of the same age.

It must be stressed that many women do not necessarily have orgasms during sexual activity with a partner. However this by no means detracts from their enjoyment of sex or diminishes the strength of the relationship they have with their partner. It is not our intention to convey what might be criticized as a biased 'orgasmocentric' view of female sexuality.

Summary of Section 3.4

1   In both women and men, the peripheral index of arousal is the filling of genital structures with blood. Erection of both the clitoris and the penis are caused by filling of blood vessels and blood spaces within the genitals.

2   The small arteries that supply blood to the genitals are normally constricted. In sexual arousal, they are dilated by the relaxation of smooth muscle in the vessel walls.

3   The state of smooth muscle contraction or relaxation is determined by activity within neurons of the sympathetic and parasympathetic nervous systems.

4   Activity within the neurons that innervate the smooth muscle is determined by both local and central events.

5   Male erectile dysfunction can be caused by multiple interacting factors, both local (e.g. atherosclerosis) and central (e.g. anxiety about sexual performance). An analogous condition in females is failure of engorgement of the genitals.

6   In certain cases, the organic versus psychogenic dichotomy for explaining erectile dysfunction can have some validity. However, sharp demarcation can also disguise the interactions that are inherent in the system, as represented in Figure 3.1.

3.5 Exogenous chemicals and sexual behaviour

3.5.1 Chemical effects and placebo effects

Researchers have investigated the effects of alcohol (i.e. ethanol) on sexual arousal (Rosen, 1991). Different doses of alcohol were given and subsequent reactions to an erotic film measured: in men, penile tumescence, heart rate and the subject's self report of arousal. Heart rate showed a linear increase with the quantity of alcohol ingested. In one study, a slight increase in tumescence was measured at low alcohol doses but as the dose was increased, so tumescence was observed to decrease. Subjective measures of arousal (i.e. the subject's own reported feeling) mirrored the decrease in tumescence. However, in another study, subjects reported a belief that alcohol enhanced sexual performance in spite of the fact that they were exhibiting a lower tumescence as a result of the alcohol ingestion.

Further studies have looked at the effects of beliefs. Subjects are divided into four groups, which are given the following treatments and then shown an erotic film:

- Group 1 given alcohol; told they are getting alcohol
- Group 2 given alcohol; told they are getting tonic water
- Group 3 given tonic water; told they are getting tonic water
- Group 4 given tonic water; told they are getting alcohol

In spite of the negative pharmacological effect of the alcohol on tumescence, there was evidence for heightened tumescence in Group 1 as compared to Group 2, and in Group 4 as compared to Group 3. This shows the importance of the expectation of an effect as learned through culture, a so-called **placebo effect** (discussed in more detail in Chapter 4).

In an experiment similar to that just described for men, women were given various quantities of alcohol to drink, followed by presentation of an erotic film. The state of vaginal engorgement was measured and subjective reports of arousal were also collected. Physiologically similar effects to those of men were obtained, i.e. as the quantity of alcohol increased, so the magnitude of the blood flow to the genitals decreased. However, for women, the subjective reports indicated increasing arousal as a function of increasing levels of alcohol.

3.5.2 Chemicals and long-term dysfunction

There is both a short-term (shortly following ingestion) and a serious long-term (even during abstinent periods) deterioration of male erectile function in alcoholics. In part, this is caused by a failure in the production of testosterone (inhibited by alcohol) and in part by the directly damaging effects of alcohol on the central and peripheral neurons involved. Alcohol can damage the neurons that form the local circuit underlying erectile function. Also, in large amounts, alcohol is known to alter long-term patterns of neurotransmission. For reasons that remain unclear, elevated levels of the female hormones oestrogen (from the adrenal cortex) and prolactin (from the pituitary gland) have been observed in alcoholic males; both these hormones are known from other studies to lower desire and erectile function.

Ethanol has inhibitory effects at various levels of the hypothalamic–pituitary–gonadal system. For example, it decreases the number of gonadotropin (FSH and LH) receptors at the testes.

❑   What effect would this be expected to have?

▪   Since the gonadotropins stimulate the testes to produce testosterone (Chapter 2), a reduction in the rate of release of testosterone is predicted.

Ethanol also acts at the level of the hypothalamus and pituitary gland to depress activity in the system. The effects of chronic alcohol use in females are less clear: some investigators report little effect but others report severe dysfunction.

A number of other commonly used drugs, e.g. nicotine, marijuana and opiates, suppress the synthesis of testosterone by the testes. Thus, although their immediate effects might well be to heighten sexual arousal and enjoyment, the long-term effects of chronic use might be to decrease its capacity. Of course, the user might be expected to associate the drug more closely with the short-term positive effects rather than with the long-term negative effects.

Understandably, there is a demand for drugs that can help to improve sexual function. There is some evidence that the therapeutic drug apomorphine, a dopamine agonist, can improve erectile response in males suffering from dysfunction (Rosen, 1991). It seems to do so by its action on dopamine receptors in the brain.

Summary of Section 3.5

1   In both men and women, alcohol (ethanol) exerts a negative pharmacological effect on the process of genital engorgement with blood. However, in an experiment on men it was shown that the knowledge or belief that the subject was getting alcohol exerted a positive placebo effect on arousal.

2   Excessive alcohol intake can damage the erectile process by: (a) reducing testosterone secretion, (b) affecting patterns of neural transmission and (c) damaging neurons directly involved in penile erection.

3   Drugs can exert an immediate positive effect upon sexual arousal and enjoyment but may have a long-term negative effect. The user is most likely to register the short-term effect.

3.6 Ageing and women's sexuality

Menopause, which now occurs at an average age of around 51 years, represents the transition from having a system which can serve a reproductive function to a state without that function. For sexuality, there are important hormonal consequences of this transition. In addition, there are important effects mediated by cultural transmission of information. For example, knowledge that reproduction is no longer possible might bring relief from the fear of pregnancy and contribute to a heightened sexual interest. Alternatively, this might have the opposite effect, i.e. engender negative feelings of being 'less female' than before the menopause.

Prior to the menopause, the ovaries are the source of about 95% of the oestrogen that appears in the bloodstream. Following the menopause, this source of oestrogen is stopped. It was once believed that events at the ovary itself (e.g. reduction in number of follicles present) were wholly responsible for this transition. However, more recent evidence has shown that there are also other changes implicated.

❑   What might these be?

■   Changes at the hypothalamus and the pituitary gland play a role;
      neural and ovarian changes are jointly involved.

Corresponding to the menopause, the ovaries lose sensitivity to the
pituitary hormones FSH and LH, which results in a decreased oestrogen
output. This is followed by increased FSH and LH concentrations in the
blood.

❑   Does this suggest that a negative feedback pathway is implicated in
      this effect?

■   Yes: oestrogen inhibits FSH and LH secretion.

As was noted earlier, both the ovaries and the adrenal glands are able to
synthesize and secrete androgens. Post-menopausal women have lower
androgen levels than pre-menopausal women. However, the ovary
continues to secrete testosterone in some 50% of post-menopausal women.
In women, as in men, testosterone exerts its primary effect upon cognitive
and motivational processes involving desire and fantasy, rather than on the
genitals (Sherwin, 1991).

The tissues of the reproductive system are affected by oestrogen and so,
when the source of oestrogen is drastically lowered at menopause, changes
occur there. (As noted in Chapter 2, oestrogen continues to be produced
after the menopause, by the adrenal glands, but at a low level.) Oestrogen
causes relaxation of the smooth muscle in the walls of blood vessels (i.e.
vasodilation), thereby increasing blood flow. At menopause, there is a
decrease in vascularity (reduction in number of blood vessels) of the
vaginal epithelium. There is also a decrease in vaginal lubrication, which
can result in uncomfortable or even painful intercourse. These factors make
it likely that, as a result of local oestrogen-dependent processes, there can
be a negative effect upon sexual functioning in post-menopausal women.

Hormone replacement therapy (HRT) offers a means of observing the
effects of hormones on sexual functioning (though such supplementary
hormone treatment is not without potential problems for a significant
number of women). This can compensate for the loss of the natural source
of reproductive hormones at menopause or for that incurred as a result of
removal of the ovaries from pre-menopausal women. HRT can be
administered orally (in tablet form) or by the implantation subcutaneously
(i.e. under the skin) of pellets that contain oestradiol (an oestrogen),
testosterone and progesterone. The pellets then provide a steady release of
hormones over the subsequent months. Studies have reported increases in
libido, initiation of sexual activity and enjoyment of sex, following such
treatment.

It is commonly reported in the popular media for both men and women
that an active sex life throughout the earlier years correlates positively with

the maintenance of sexual function in older age. This is sometimes summarized in lay language, in common with similar potential declines in intellect and capacity for physical activity, as 'use it or lose it'. Investigators have found this indeed to be the case; for both men and women, past interest in sex and frequency of sexual contact correlate positively with the continuation of sexual activity in old age. In ageing women, there is also a positive correlation between, on the one hand, socio-economic status and educational level and, on the other, level of sexual activity. This might be because of a better level of general health but also be due perhaps to less restraint and more flexibility of behaviour. The loss of sexual function which often occurs with ageing might owe as much to the glamorization of youth and to the assumption within society that the elderly are asexual and undesirable partners, as to any intrinsic biological decline.

Summary of Section 3.6

1   Tissues of the female reproductive system are affected by oestrogen. When the level of oestrogen is reduced at menopause, changes occur at the genitals. There is a decrease in both vascularity and lubrication of the vaginal epithelium and this can make intercourse uncomfortable or even painful.

2   As a result of local oestrogen-dependent processes, there can be a negative effect upon sexual functioning in post-menopausal women.

3   Hormone replacement therapy (HRT) can compensate for the loss of hormones at menopause or for that incurred as a result of removal of the ovaries from pre-menopausal women. Following such treatment, there are often increases in libido, initiation of sexual activtiy and enjoyment of sex.

3.7 Conclusions

In trying to understand sexual motivation and behaviour, it is crucial to keep the idea expressed in Figure 3.1 in mind, involving a circle of causes. Bancroft (1989) argues a similar point to this and refers to sexual dysfunction as breaking of a point in the circle between the central factors and the genital response. However, although the dysfunction might initially be localizable to a particular point in the circle, the effects would normally be felt *throughout the circle*. Even after a local effect is corrected there might be lasting effects throughout the circle. For example, painful sex as a result of vaginal discomfort might leave lasting negative memories that outlive restoration of local function. Erectile dysfunction as a result of excess alcohol consumption on a few occasions might provoke anxiety of failure that long outlasts the effect of the alcohol.

The circle usually involves another individual or, to be more exact, there are generally two interacting circles of causal relationships for two individuals. Just as the subtlety of this dynamic interaction is what can give sex its uniquely pleasurable aspect, so it gives much opportunity for dysfunction.

As has been noted already in the course, trying to find a definition of health that we can all agree with is problematic. Related to sexual function, a term like 'sexual health' or 'sexual well-being' is even more difficult since it necessarily involves complex interactions between individuals, with social and moral connotations. A definition of sexual well-being given simply in terms of potency and mechanical function would seem inadequate, though that is not to deny that loss of such function can have serious implications for well-being. As far as we know, the effect on well-being of sexual dysfunction is not in terms of any obvious physiological change in the body that arises directly from lack of sexual outlet. Loss of well-being is more to be understood in terms of personal frustration and disharmony in bonds formed with another person.

In considering the contribution to sexual well-being that comes from an adequate performance of sexual function, then the advice for maintaining this function is essentially that which applies to general good health. Thus emphasis would be upon the avoidance of smoking and excess alcohol, the taking of adequate exercise and observation of diet so as to avoid atherosclerosis and obesity. On a psychological level, the advice concerns the importance of maintaining harmony with others and the avoidance of conflict and stress, the topic of Chapter 5 of this book.

Objectives for Chapter 3

After completing this chapter you should be able to:

3.1 Define and use, or recognize definitions and applications of, each of the terms printed in **bold** in the text.

3.2 Explain the nature of the interactions between central (brain) and peripheral (genital) factors in sexual motivation and behaviour. (*Questions 3.1, 3.2 and 3.3*)

3.3 Discuss the ways in which there are special complicating features about human sexuality as compared to that of non-human animals. (*Question 3.4*)

3.4 Explain the importance of developmental factors for understanding adult sexuality and relate this to the action of hormones. (*Question 3.3*)

3.5 Outline some of the factors that serve to switch on sexual motivation and some of those that serve to switch it off, relating these to neural processes. (*Question 3.6*)

3.6 Show how sexual dysfunction might be understood by some of the processes discussed in the chapter. (*Question 3.1*)

Questions for Chapter 3

Question 3.1 (*Objective 3.2 and 3.6*)

Some researchers speak of a circle of sexual arousal, and of sexual dysfunction as being a breaking of the circle. What might be meant by this? Would it be more appropriate to consider dysfunction in terms of the formation of a *vicious circle* of effects?

Question 3.2 (*Objective 3.2*)

Based upon Figure 3.6, you can imagine other neurons comparable to neuron 4 and the post-ganglionic neuron with which it makes synaptic contact, but part of the sympathetic nervous system. What would be the predicted effect of injecting an agonist to the neurotransmitter that these sympathetic post-ganglionic neurons release at the neuromuscular junction?

Question 3.3 (*Objective 3.2*)

Based upon Figure 3.6 and in terms of the activity in neurons 1, 5 and 6, what is the pattern of activation that will maximize activity in neuron 3 and thereby neuron 4?

Question 3.4 (*Objective 3.3*)

In what ways are there general properties of the processes underlying sexual motivation that might be applicable to a number of animal species, including humans? In what ways might you expect that the possession of a complex language and culture by humans makes these processes more complicated than in the case of non-human animals?

Question 3.5 (*Objective 3.4*)

Recall from Book 2, Chapter 3, the definition of a hormone. Relate this definition to the terms 'organizing' and 'activational' in the context of the human sexuality.

Question 3.6 (*Objective 3.5*)

In the context of synaptic transmission, what is meant by the term 'antagonist'? Illustrate your answer by reference to Figure 3.4.

References

Bancroft, J. (1989) *Human Sexuality and its Problems*, Churchill Livingstone, Edinburgh.

Beatty, W. W. (1992) Gonadal hormones and sex differences in nonreproductive behaviours, in *Handbook of Behavioural Neurobiology*, vol. 11, *Sexual Differentiation*, A. A. Gerall, H. Moltz and I. L. Ward (eds), Plenum Press, New York, pp. 85–128.

Buvat, J., Buvat-Herbaut, M., Lemaire, A., Marcolin, G. and Quittelier, E. (1990) Recent developments in the clinical assessment and diagnosis of erectile dysfunction, in *Annual Review of Sex Research*, **1**, J. Bancroft (ed), The Society of Sex Research, pp. 265–308.

Everitt, B. J. and Bancroft, J. (1991) Of rats and men: the comparative approach to male sexuality, in *Annual Review of Sex Research*, **2**, J. Bancroft (ed), Society for the Scientific Study of Sex, pp. 77–117.

Hoon, P. W., Wincze, J. P. and Hoon, E. F. (1976) Physiological assessment of sexual arousal in women, *Psychophysiology*, **13**, 196–204.

Myers, L.S. and Morokoff, P. J. (1986) Physiological and subjective sexual arousal in pre- and postmenopausal women and postmenopausal women taking replacement therapy, *Psychophysiology*, **23**, 283–292.

Rodriguez-Manzo, G. and Fernandez-Guasti, A. (1994) Reversal of sexual exhaustion by serotonergic and noradrenergic agents, *Behavioural Brain Research*, **62**, 127–134.

Rosen, R. C. (1991) Alcohol and drug effects on sexual response: human experimental and clinical studies, in *Annual Review of Sex Research*, **2**, J. Bancroft (ed), Society for the Scientific Study of Sex, pp. 119–179.

Sherwin, B. B. (1991) The psychoendocrinology of aging and female sexuality, in *Annual Review of Sex Research*, **2**, J. Bancroft (ed), Society for the Scientific Study of Sex, pp. 181–198.

Tobet, S. A. and Fox, T. O. (1992) Sex differences in neuronal morphology influenced hormonally throughout life, in *Handbook of Behavioural Neurobiology*, vol. 11, *Sexual Differentiation*, A. Gerall, H. Moltz and I. L. Ward (eds), Plenum Press, New York, pp. 41–83.

CHAPTER 4
PAIN

4.1 Introduction

All of us probably know only too well what is meant by pain. Attempts at scientific definitions, such as:

> *Pain is an unpleasant sensory and emotional experience associated with actual or potential tissue damage, or described in terms of such damage. (International Association for the Study of Pain)*

can do little more than to formalize that which is common knowledge.

Much of the quest of both the medical community and sections of the lay public is concerned with the alleviation of pain (termed **analgesia**) by, for example, the use of drugs (termed *analgesics*) or by hypnosis. Pain is, however, not simply an unmitigated evil, much as it might seem so. Rather, it can be of crucial value to survival. For example, by resting an injured limb as a reaction to pain, we increase the chances of recovery of the limb. By retiring to bed with the pain of a headache, as in influenza, we aid our recovery. The adaptive value of pain is brought home to us by the rare individual who is born lacking a sensitivity to pain. An example was the Canadian girl, known as Miss C, whose case is well documented (Melzack and Wall, 1982). Miss C failed to perform some common actions, e.g. to shift her weight around when standing and to turn over in bed. These are normal reactions to discomfort and help to protect us from damage to joints, skin, etc. Clearly, a behavioural process that protects us from tissue damage by not only *reacting to* damage but also *preempting* it is important for our survival.

Theologians and sceptics have long argued over the implications of the existence of pain although, on reflection, it is difficult to imagine how we could function without the help of such a sensation. Pain prevents us from engaging in certain activities that could prove harmful. At a time of tissue damage, our own intellectual reasoning as to what is best for us might be little match for the temptations to 'get up and go', even at the risk of exacerbating the damage. But an excruciating pain will counterbalance if not kill most passions for action.

You might be able to appreciate that the pain of a hangover headache or a sprained ankle clearly has adaptive value. However, how can the chronic pain of, say, cancer be said to be biologically useful? An attempt at explaining this might be twofold. Firstly, biological adaptation cannot be expected to account for every instance of pain. We are equipped with the capacity to feel pain in most parts of our body and it would be maladaptive not to do so. Given this basic design, which serves us well in most situations, there are bound to be some situations for which it does not behave adaptively. Chronic pain might be seen as a stretching of otherwise adaptive processes outside their normal adaptive range of limited duration. By analogy, the basic design of the feeding control system has served us well throughout evolution, at times of abundance and shortage, but it will not behave adaptively in every respect when confronted with late 20th century Western living, surrounded by an abundance of fatty and sugary foods.

The other aspect of the argument is that much pain comes in later years, when we are past the age at which reproduction has normally taken place. Hence, in our evolutionary history it would not necessarily have been a disadvantage in terms of perpetuating our genes. Indeed, some pains would seem to be inadequate for our own good. For example, the pain of an occasional hangover headache seems too little to deter excessive drinking except for a day or so. Taking a morning-after 'super-drug' to take away such headaches might only hasten our demise.

Given that tissues are susceptible to damage, evolution has found two different sorts of solution to the problem of how to defend them. First, we have some fast reflexes, organized locally at the level of the spinal cord, that are responsible for removal of part of the body (e.g. a limb) from the source of tissue damage. The formation and function of these reflexes is largely genetically determined, 'wired in' and 'ready to go'. The reflex consists of detectors of tissue damage which trigger activity in appropriate motor neurons, so as to distance the body region from the noxious stimulus. The reflexes occur even before we consciously feel pain.

Over and above such local protective reflexes, we have the pain system, organized centrally, in the brain, with motivational and emotional colouring, i.e. there is an unpleasant subjective conscious experience that forms the focus of attention. The pain system enables us to find flexible and even creative solutions to tissue damage. Pain motivates our whole-body, goal-directed behaviour. The behavioural solution is selected on the basis of whether it diminishes pain. Imagine writhing around in bed in pain. In one particular position you find that pain is minimized and so you attempt to hold that position. The pain system also gives us the facility to recruit social help: we hope that others will empathize with us and bring comfort because we have all shared such a common experience.

Summary of Section 4.1

1   The bases of pain can be understood in terms of their adaptive value.

2   Analgesics act to counter pain.

3   Chronic pain is a grossly exaggerated activation, i.e. lasting over abnormally long time periods, of otherwise adaptive processes.

4   Some fast, automatic spinal reflexes protect us from local damage and their activation precedes the sensation of pain.

5   Pain offers the possibility of flexible solutions to tissue damage.

4.2 An early attempt at explaining pain

How do we begin to explain pain scientifically? The French philosopher René Descartes (1595–1650) was perhaps the first to propose a scientific theory of pain (Melzack, 1993). Although the precise details might appear bizarre today (e.g. Descartes didn't know about neurons and action potentials), the principles developed by Descartes were widely accepted in the subsequent years. Today, some 300 years on, we have inherited much of Descartes' theory, but we have also been able to identify its fundamental flaws. So a logical starting point for the present chapter is to consider briefly what Descartes proposed and then later sections will return to it, to show where it is correct and also where it needs to change.

Figure 4.1a summarizes the theory. Noxious stimuli are detected by receptors and messages are sent to the brain which then effects withdrawal actions to remove the limb from the offending object.

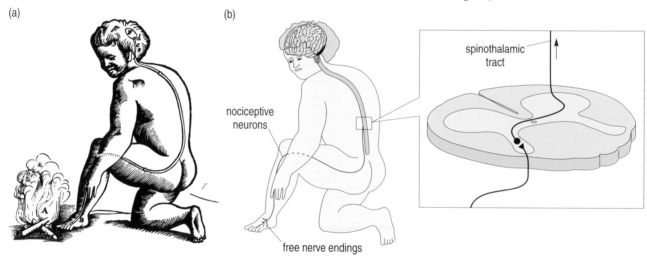

Figure 4.1   The concept of pain: (a) as proposed by René Descartes (note the direct connection between the periphery and a pain centre in the brain); (b) a modern-day version of Descartes' concept.

❑   Do you see any reason to qualify Descartes' theory?

■   Withdrawal of the limb would normally occur as a result of a local spinal reflex, before a sensation of pain is felt. Though, if the reflex were to fail, the brain could consciously organize removal of the limb on the basis of pain perception.

❑   What advantage is offered by having withdrawal organized in such local reflexes, rather than involving the brain in the initial reaction?

■   Speed. It takes time for an action potential to travel along an axon, and the site of damage (e.g. a toe) might be some way from the brain. Think of the distance involved in getting to the brain and then back down to the muscle.

Descartes was correct in his proposal of a pathway that carries information about noxious stimuli from the periphery to the brain. A comparison of Descartes' ideas and an important feature of a modern understanding (Figure 4.1b) shows this. Note the nociceptive neurons (see Book 2, Chapters 3 and 4), which convey information from the periphery to the spinal cord. There are free nerve endings at the end of the fibre. It is these that are sensitive to tissue damage. Note also the synapse made within the spinal cord. A further neuron then conveys the message to the brain as part of a fibre tract running up the spinal cord, termed the *spinothalamic tract*.

Although the reflex organizes limb withdrawal, the pathway to the brain would be responsible for instigating subsequent action to care for the foot. Also, one hopes, as a result of this information being processed in the brain, a memory would be formed, the person would learn and thereby avoid fires in the future (see Figure 4.1a).

The influence of Descartes' theory has been immense. Experiments on pain during the last 100 years have been characterized by a search for: (a) particular pathways that carry noxious information from the periphery to the brain; and (b) a pain centre in the brain. In other words, pain was traditionally viewed as a straightforward conduction system for conveying signals from periphery to brain centre. Pain was seen as the outcome of activation of specific receptors and was experienced in proportion to the activity in a specific pathway.

Patients who reported pain, but for whom no organic disorder could be found, simply didn't fit the theory and in some cases tended to be referred to psychiatrists and/or regarded as malingerers (Melzack, 1993). It is not difficult to see why such phenomena are problematic for a simple-pathway model of pain. How we might understand such phenomena will be discussed in Section 4.7.2. Before we go on to such theorizing, the next section will consider some neurons that play a crucial role in pain and will show that, in at least one way, Descartes got it right.

Summary of Section 4.2

1   Traditionally, theories of pain proposed a straightforward conduction system running from the periphery to the brain.

2   The problem with the traditional models is that pain often does not show a simple relationship with tissue damage.

4.3 The sensory input

We know that throughout most of the body there are nociceptive neurons, whose tips are sensitive to tissue damage (See Figure 4.1b). The tips are termed *nociceptors*. These neurons have a high threshold, meaning that it is relatively difficult to trigger action potentials in them. Their axons have a small diameter and are often termed **small-diameter fibres**. Tissue damage, either of the tip itself or in the vicinity of the tip, is the necessary stimulus to trigger activity in the nociceptor. Non-noxious stimulation is inadequate. Chemicals are released by damaged cells and these increase the chances that action potentials will arise in nociceptive neurons whose tips are nearby. Since such neurons are specifically sensitive to noxious information, they are often termed pain receptors. However, this expression is inherently misleading. Pain is not something 'out there' to be detected, but rather a complex sensation organized by the brain. So the term nociceptor (originally meaning detector of noxious stimuli) is more accurate.

There are other neurons whose tips are in the same area of body surface and which run in parallel with the small-diameter fibres. These neurons are of larger diameter (often termed **large-diameter fibres**) and have a lower threshold of activation. They too can be activated by noxious stimulation but even innocuous stimuli, such as touch, are enough to trigger activity in them.

As shown in Figure 4.2, both types of neuron make synapses in the dorsal horn of the spinal cord, although the large-diameter neurons make synapses further inside. They trigger activity in further neurons which then convey messages up the spinal cord to the brain. As will be shown in a moment there are also neurons within the local site of the spinal cord that process incoming noxious and innocuous messages.

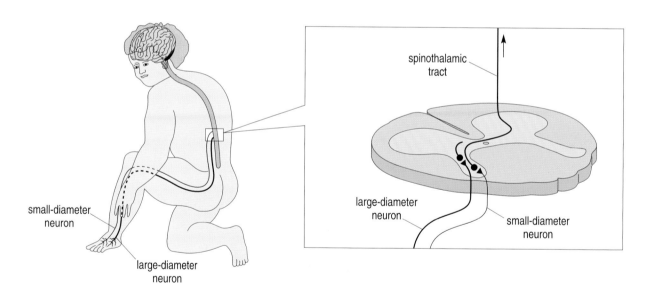

Figure 4.2   Representation of both nociceptor (tip of small–diameter neuron) and detector of innocuous touch (tip of large-diameter neuron) at the foot. Information is conveyed to the central nervous system. In this case, both neurons detect information from the same region of the body. Note that they terminate in slightly different regions of the spinal cord.

When we consider the role of pain in the organization of behaviour it might seem logical that activity in nociceptive neurons is both necessary and sufficient for the experience of pain and such reasoning has doubtless seemed attractive over the years. Indeed, under some circumstances, activity in such neurons correlates very well with the sensation of pain. However, as just noted, there are examples of pain perception that seriously complicate this simple picture.

Logically, if it is possible to identify a sensory pathway whose activation is necessary for pain perception, then the way to cure pain is to make a surgical lesion at some point in that pathway. By analogy, the sensation of vision would be lost by severing the optic nerve. Indeed, surgical intervention for intractable pain was guided by just such a principle of cutting a specific pathway. However, we now know that in most cases the pain returns some time after the surgical lesion is made (Melzack, 1993).

These days we have come to realize the subtle complexity of pain. It is not always neatly related one-to-one to tissue damage. Rather, we now know that there can be a strong sensation of pain with little evidence of tissue damage. Conversely, there can be tissue damage with little pain. In the so-called 'placebo response' there can be a relief of pain brought about by taking medicine of completely arbitrary content in association with beliefs as to its efficacy. So, as with the other topics discussed in this course, we arrive at a complex system with various interacting factors playing a role. The chapter will attempt to guide you to an understanding of these multiple factors involved in pain. The next section will look at a theory that can start to accommodate this evidence.

Summary of Section 4.3

1   Nociceptive neurons are specialized, small-diameter, high-threshold neurons whose tips are sensitive to tissue damage.

2   Large-diameter neurons are sensitive to both noxious and non-noxious stimuli.

3   Both neuron types form synapses in the dorsal horn of the spinal cord, although the large-diameter neurons make synapses further inside.

4   Although nociceptive neurons are sensitive to tissue damage, the sensation of pain sometimes correlates poorly with their activity.

4.4 The gate theory

4.4.1 Basics of the theory

What is termed the **gate theory** of pain was first proposed by Melzack and Wall in 1965. It is represented in Figure 4.3. The assumptions that are incorporated into the theory are as follows (Melzack, 1993):

1   As was shown in Figure 4.1b and 4.2, there are small–diameter afferent fibres (nociceptive neurons) which make a synapse with neurons in the spinal cord. These particular spinal cord neurons are termed **T cells**, for transmission cells (not to be confused with T cells of the immune system). The essence of the theory is that the capacity of activity in the nociceptive neuron to excite the T cell is not constant. Rather, this capacity is altered by what is metaphorically termed a 'gating mechanism' in the spinal cord (see Figure 4.3).

2   The state of opening and closing of the gate is affected by the ratio of activity in the large–diameter (L) to that in the small–diameter (S) fibres, arising in the same region of the body (e.g. a region of foot as shown in Figure 4.2). If the gate is open, action potentials in the small–diameter afferent neurons are effective in instigating action potentials in the T cells. Activity in the large–diameter neurons tends to close the gate.

❑   What does it mean to say that the gate is closed?

■   Even if the small–diameter neurons are active, this activity would fail to have much, if any, effect on the T cells.

3   Apart from the effect on gate closing of the ratio of L/S diameter activities, the gate can be closed by activity in a descending pathway from the brain (see Figure 4.3c).

4   There are cognitive processes in the brain which, by means of the descending pathway described in 3, are able to influence the gating process.

5   When the activity in the T cells exceeds a certain threshold, pain is normally experienced.

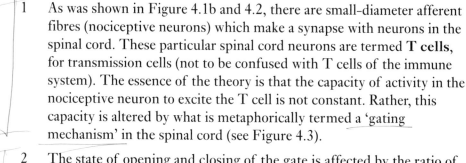

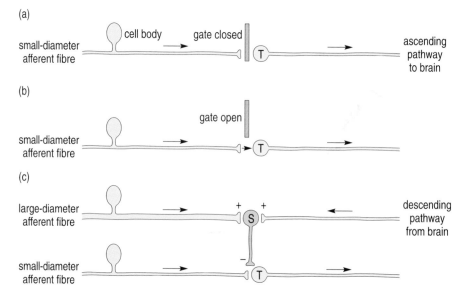

Figure 4.3   The gate theory of pain: (a) representation of gate closed; (b) representation of gate open; (c) more realistic representation, showing neurons involved in the gate.

Note in Figure 4.3c that a small neuron (S) within the local region of the spinal cord controls the state of opening and closing of the gate. This is shown (in red) with a minus sign attached, indicating that activity in neuron S serves to inhibit the synapse at which substance P is the transmitter (Figure 4.4). The neuron S is excited (plus signs) by activity in either the large-diameter afferent fibre or a descending pathway from the brain or both. It is possible to speculate on the nature of the inhibition from neuron S; Figure 4.4 suggests that a type of **opioid** is involved. Opioids are a class of substances that include morphine, heroin and the naturally produced enkephalins, all of which have similar chemical properties. They are all analgesics. In this case, enkephalin is the chemical released by neuron S to occupy opioid receptors at either the terminal of the small-diameter afferent fibre or the cell body of the T cell or both.

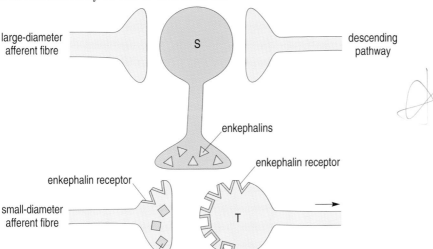

Figure 4.4   Representation of the possible mode of action of enkephalin released from neuron S. Substance P is released from the nociceptive neuron and occupies sites on the T cell. Its presence excites the T cell.

It is interesting to speculate as to why the nervous system is constructed in such a way that large-diameter fibres serve to inhibit the effect of activity in nociceptive neurons. One (tentatively proposed) possibility lies deep in our evolutionary history. Because of the pain-reducing effect of such stimulation, it might encourage the licking of wounds and thereby their cleaning.

One can also speculate as to why there is a descending inhibitory pathway. Possibly, at times it can be useful to inhibit the effect of nociceptive messages, e.g. when fleeing injured from a predator. Indeed, much clinical experience suggests that even serious injury, suffered for instance on a battlefield, is not accompanied by pain until the victim is away from the danger zone. Athletes sometimes persist with a contest in the face of tissue injury.

4.4.2 Implications of the gate theory

By the mid-1970s, the gate theory had achieved respectability and had taken its place in the standard textbooks of psychobiology and medical science.

The postulate of a gate that was influenced in part by psychological factors was of enormous importance. On the theoretical and conceptual level, it helped to bridge the gap between physiology and psychology. Theorists could think in terms of an integration of evidence from different sources. A unified concept seemed possible. There need be no more simple dichotomies between real pain, as the responsibility of medicine, and imagined pain, as the inevitable responsibility of psychiatrists.

On a practical and clinical level, the gate formed a natural focus for thinking about how interventions for pain might work. For instance, one could address the traditional Chinese technique of acupuncture. According to Chinese theory, acupuncture is said to work by balancing the so-called 'Yin' and 'Yang' which are forces thought to exist in nature. To Western sceptical scientists, such a notion sounds unscientific. However, by means of the gate theory, we can investigate the possibility that the pain-relieving effects of acupuncture might operate in some way through closing the gate (Filshie and Morrison, 1988). Thus we might hope for some integration between Eastern and Western medical traditions. Indeed, Western scientists have investigated acupuncture to see whether it is a means of stimulating the body's endogenous opioid system.

❑   How might you ascertain whether acupuncture works by increasing the production of natural opioids?

◼   One way is to see whether the effect is abolished by injecting an opioid antagonist (see Book 2, Chapter 3).

Melzack poses the question as to what is the gate theory's main contribution to knowledge and suggests:

> *I believe it was the emphasis on CNS mechanisms. The theory forced the medical and biological sciences to accept the brain as an active system that filters, selects and modulates inputs. The dorsal horns, too, were not merely passive transmission stations but sites at which dynamic activities – inhibition, excitation and modulation – occurred. The theory highlighted the central nervous system as an essential component in pain processes. (Melzack, 1993)*

Later sections of this chapter will look at some of the phenomena of pain. In so doing, the discussion will be illuminated by the gate theory.

Summary of Section 4.4

1   According to gate theory, the relationship between activity in nociceptive neurons (small–diameter neurons) and spinal cord T cells depends upon the activity in other neurons. Metaphorically expressed, this constitutes a gate.

2   Activity in large-diameter afferent neurons and a descending pathway serves to close the gate.

4.5 Referred pain

Referred pain is a somewhat bizarre phenomenon that some of you might have experienced. If there is a source of tissue damage at one location in the body, it can sometimes be experienced ('referred to') a completely different location. For example, pain which really corresponds to tissue damage (or threat of it) at the heart (for example, angina) might be experienced as emanating from the left shoulder and arm. The pain arising from a kidney stone can be referred to the genitals.

Such a pattern is not haphazard but reflects the developmental origin of the neurons involved. For example, nociceptors at the heart will trigger the same T cells as those arising at the left shoulder and arm. Figure 4.5 illustrates a possible basis to such a process. Note the individual T cell in the dorsal horn of the spinal cord, which is excited by neurons from both an internal organ and a region of skin.

Although it is clear that such a pooling of inputs would give a basis for there to be confusion, why should, say, the skin dominate over the heart in the interpretation? Why, conversely, are pains with origin at the skin not just as often referred to the heart? A possible answer is in terms of our familiarity with pains. We all encounter pains of superficial origin (e.g. banging ones arm on a shelf) and they make good sense to us. We know that for tactile stimulation there is a well-defined relationship between body region stimulated and area of somatosensory cortex activated – the sensory homunculus (see Book 2, Chapter 3). Thus when stimuli from the heart activate similar brain regions, we interpret it as the more familiar event.

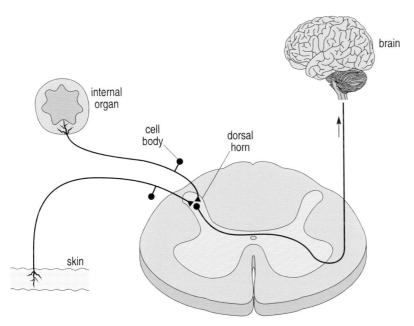

Figure 4.5 A suggested neural basis of the phenomenon of referred pain.

Summary of Section 4.5

1   Pain that is triggered by tissue damage at one body region can be referred to a different region, a phenomenon known as referred pain.

2   An example of referred pain is that arising from tissue damage at the heart, but which is felt in the left shoulder and arm.

4.6 Analgesic techniques

4.6.1 Stimulation of large-diameter fibres

Since the model shows that stimulation of the large-diameter fibres serves to close the gate, then therapeutic intervention involving excitation of such fibres is suggested. Long before the scientific study of pain, humans discovered for themselves a relationship between such stimulation and analgesia. It is undoubtedly everyone's experience that rubbing a painful site (e.g. a mosquito bite) tends to reduce the pain. Presumably, it does so by means of stimulation of low-threshold large-diameter fibres whose tips are in the region of the bite alongside the nociceptors that are causing the problem. On a more formal level, the gate theory has inspired techniques that involve electrical stimulation of regions of the body that are causing pain (the TENS technique, discussed in Chapter 2).

4.6.2 Chemical analgesics

Analgesic substances are injected, swallowed or applied locally to the skin. Their action can be either peripheral or central. An example of a peripherally acting analgesic is aspirin. It blocks the synthesis of **prostaglandins**. Prostaglandins released at the site of tissue damage normally sensitize the nociceptor, making it more likely that tissue damage will initiate action potentials. Aspirin lowers the probability of the generation of action potentials and thereby initiation of the nociceptive signal (see Figure 4.6b). Action potentials are an all-or-none event; they either occur or they don't (see Book 2, Chapter 3). Aspirin alters the frequency with which they arise, not their amplitude.

A drug such as Lignocaine acts to block sodium channels in the membrane of the neuron. Lignocaine, or something similar, is what you might have been given as a local anaesthetic when visiting the dentist.

❑   Imagine an injection of Lignocaine made at a point between B and C in Figure 4.6c. What will be the effect on action potentials travelling along the neuron from the tip towards the spinal cord? Compare this with the effect of aspirin.

■   You should recall from Book 2, Chapter 3, that the action potential involves a movement of sodium ions into the neuron. If the sodium channels are blocked in a section of membrane, the action potentials will be unable to pass this region of the neuron and so will terminate there.

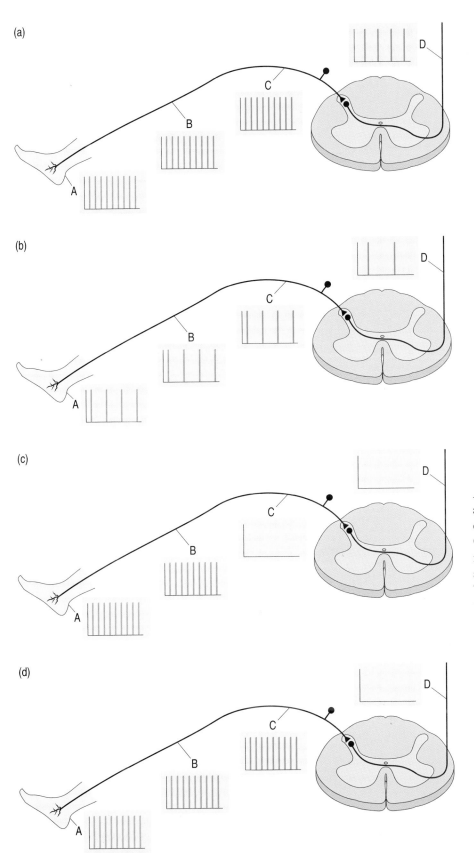

Figure 4.6   The action of aspirin, Lignocaine and opioids on the nervous system. (a) Control (i.e. the situation immediately prior to administration of analgesic). (b) The action of aspirin in blocking the synthesis of prostaglandins. Note that the frequency of action potentials arising at the tip (A) and observed at two points along the length of the nociceptor (B and C) is less as a result of the action of aspirin. Note also the reduction in frequency of action potentials in the T cell (location D). (c) The action of Lignocaine, after injection at a point between locations B and C. (d) The action of opioids on the nervous system after injection. Note that activity in the T cell is lowered but not that in the nociceptive neuron.

Figure 4.6c shows the effect of injecting Lignocaine. The action potential comes to an end at the region where the sodium channels are blocked. Note that Lignocaine tends to block sodium channels in neurons of all kinds in the region injected, not only those carrying noxious information. Therefore, after a visit to the dentist, you will tend to feel numb in the mouth region and have difficulty in initiating movements there. The effect of aspirin, on the other hand, is more specific to nociceptive neurons; it leaves other neurons unaffected because it targets prostaglandin synthesis.

Finally, there are analgesic substances that act upon the central nervous system directly. The opioids, e.g. heroin and morphine, are examples of such substances. Figure 4.6d shows the action of opioids. The nociceptive neuron's activity itself is unaffected even if the opioid contacts it. Occupation of receptors at the terminal of the nociceptive neuron by an opioid substance prevents action potentials that arrive at the terminal from triggering activity in the T cells. There is also activation of the descending inhibitory pathway by occupation of opioid receptors in the brain. Both of these effects make good sense in terms of the gate theory. Both actions could be described as closing the gate. Morphine can be injected either at the spinal site where action potentials in activated nociceptive neurons arrive, or into the bloodstream, wherein it is transported to the nociceptor.

Summary of Section 4.6

1 Considering sensory neurons that are associated with a particular area of skin, stimulation of large-diameter fibres can inhibit the effect of nociceptive neuron activity on T cell activity.

2 Aspirin acts as an analgesic by inhibiting the production of prostaglandins and thereby lowering the probability of an action potential arising in a nocicepive neuron.

3 The analgesic effect of Lignocaine occurs via the blocking of sodium channels in neurons.

4 Opioids act on the central nervous system by (a) blocking the capacity of nociceptive neurons to trigger T cell activity and (b) activating a descending inhibitory pathway.

4.7 Phantom limb pain

4.7.1 Introduction

One challenge that is posed to the gate theory, as to any other theory of the basis of pain, is the phenomenon of **phantom limb pain**. Commonly, people with a limb amputated still feel pain apparently in the missing limb. About 60% of amputees continue to experience phantom limb pain even at 7 years following amputation. The pain of a phantom limb is often similar to pains experienced earlier when the limb was intact (albeit damaged or injured), suggesting an important role for specific memories. However, although such memories seem to play a role, they are not essential to the experience. People born without a limb can still experience phantom sensations 'in' the missing limb.

Melzack describes the following reports from amputees:

> *I continue to feel my leg as vividly as I felt my real leg and I often feel a burning pain in my foot. (Melzack, 1989, p. 2)*

Amputees describe the phantom limb in such terms as sweaty or cold or itchy. The feeling is so real that amputees have difficulty in not stepping out of bed onto the missing limb. Points of reference associated with the limb when intact such as the pain of a sore on the foot or the tightness of a ring on a finger persist in vivid detail. Amputees with Parkinson's disease continue to perceive a tremor in the 'missing' limb. Not just limbs are felt as phantoms; following their surgical removal, the bladder, rectum, breasts and penis can all be felt just as before. Even phantom orgasms have been reported in people with a spinal cord injury that prevents sensations from the genitals reaching the brain.

Melzack describes three different situations in which the phantom limb phenomenon can be experienced. There is (1) the experience of a limb after it has been amputated, (2) the experience of a limb after its sensory input to the spinal cord has been lost or (3) an experience of both the legs and the remainder of the body corresponding to a level at the spinal cord below that at which an injury has occurred. The latter situation is illustrated in Figure 4.7. Paraplegic individuals, in whom the spinal cord has been broken into two, can still experience severe pains referred to body sites for which no neural communication with the brain is possible.

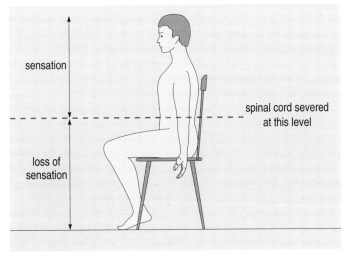

Figure 4.7   An example of where a phantom effect can arise.

4.7.2 Explaining the phenomenon

Phantom limb pain is a profound challenge for pain researchers. It seems a reasonable assumption, shared by all theorists, that the perception of pain is not a local phenomenon at the site of injury but rather involves the brain. Some contemporary theoretical models look at the brain not only as an active processor of sensory information (rather than a passive receiver) but also as something that has the intrinsic capacity to generate the pain experience even in the absence of afferent (sensory) information. Melzack's analysis leads him to four conclusions:

1   The phantom limb is very persuasive in that the sensation feels just like a real limb. Therefore, the brain processes that are activated at the time of the phantom experience are assumed to be those that would, under normal circumstances, be triggered by afferent information arising from the limb. Presumably experiences associated with the limb before the breaking of connection with the brain would have triggered the brain processes now active autonomously.

2   The processes in the brain that underlie the variety of our experiences in the world, whether painful or not, correspond to patterns of activity of neural networks in the brain. These patterns of activity are normally triggered by sensory inputs but do not always depend upon them.

3   The nervous system is responsible for the creation of a representation of the 'self' as distinct from non-self, i.e. other people and objects.

4   The brain processes that underlie the formation of a self-concept are specified genetically, though open to environmental interactions.

❑   What evidence just discussed suggests a genetic determination of the brain processes underlying pain?

■   The experience of phantom limb sensations in people born without a limb.

There exists a kind of 'neurosignature', as Melzack terms it, corresponding to our concept of a unified self. The underlying neural processes implicated in this are largely specified genetically. Within this signature, with its implication of unity and continuity of the self, there are aspects that vary according to circumstances. Thus the experience of pain is one which, during its course, gives the sense of a unified self a particular negative quality. Pleasure is a different aspect but again has a 'whole unified self' feel to the experience. Psychologists have not had a great success in understanding the more fundamental questions asked of their discipline, of the kind – what is the nature of the self? How does an integrated self sensation arise? The phantom phenomenon is useful evidence to contribute to such conceptual issues.

Interestingly, after certain brain lesions, patients have been known to reject a perfectly intact limb as not belonging; a 'non-self leg' might be thrown out of bed. A whole half of the body can be rejected as foreign. The conscious mind reacts something like the immune system: the self is accepted but the 'non-self' is rejected.

What is already clear is just how radically different the theory is from the older ones that suggested a straightforward sequence of stages of transmission, with the pattern of pain necessarily corresponding one-to-one to the pattern of afferent information in pain pathways. Thus, phantom limb pain can be understood as patterns of activity in the CNS arising in a way appropriate for noxious input, even in its absence.

One way of looking at this is to consider that in phantom phenomena not only are these neural systems denied a normal afferent input from the nociceptors but they are also without input from the benign sensory channels (e.g. the large-diameter fibres of Figures 4.2–4.4). It might be that normally such input is necessary to inhibit spontaneous activity in regions of the brain concerned with pain perception. As Melzack notes, based upon the evidence of phantom limb pain, he has been able to make some general statements about the organization of perception, for example:

> *The brain does more than detect and analyse inputs; it generates perceptual experience even when no external inputs occur. (Melzack, 1993)*

Melzack refutes the notion that:

> *…sensations are produced only by stimuli and that perceptions in the absence of stimuli are psychologically abnormal. (Melzack, 1993)*

Rather, at least in this domain, it would seem that sensory input modulates, rather than creates, the sensations that are produced by the brain.

It might be useful to view the phantom limb as a particular example of a normal functioning of the body (i.e. of the brain actively constructing experience), rather than some psychological aberration. In such terms, it would not represent abnormal brain function. It represents an aspect of how the body is felt normally, but one that is distorted, since it is without certain of the sensory inputs that normally play a part in our experience.

Melzack (1989, p. 12) suggests that there is:

> *…'filling in' of missing information on the basis of genetic programming, past experience and expectation. In short, the act of being aware of a body-self in three-dimensional space is a creative process – the product of a brain that took hundreds of millions of years to evolve. (Melzack, 1989, p. 12)*

The following section, on the placebo response, also looks at a profound challenge to conventional views of pain. An understanding of phantom limb pain might go some way to helping an understanding of the placebo effect.

Summary of Section 4.7

1   Pain felt as if it arises in a missing limb is termed phantom limb pain.

2   The existence of phantom limb pain suggests that the experience of pain is part of an active creative process organized by the brain.

4.8 The placebo effect

4.8.1 Introduction

The **placebo effect** is a powerful one that applies in a number of different areas, not just to pain (see TV programme 4, *Healing the whole*, and Chapters 1 and 3 of this book). The placebo effect has long been a part of the folklore of medicine, but sometimes proves difficult to define exactly. Here is an attempt. Suppose that a cause (X) is known to induce an effect (Y) by a process that is at least partly understood to depend upon the specific properties of X. For example, we know that a bacterial infection is cured (Y) by penicillin (X). We have reason to believe that special properties of penicillin are involved, just as we believe that special properties of heroin are involved in the pain reduction and mood change following its injection. The placebo refers to an effect similar to Y being induced by some non-specific trigger involving the patient's *belief* or *experience*, but seen even in the absence of X.

❑   Can you recall a situation where you have met the placebo effect earlier in this book?

◼   In the effect of taking alcohol on the sexual response, discussed in Chapter 3 of this book. Simply believing that one has ingested alcohol has some effect.

The placebo effect is of enormous importance. To give just one example, licensing of a new pharmaceutical would require a demonstration that its efficacy is greater than that of a placebo control substance. In a **double-blind study**, the drug would have to show a stronger effect than a placebo (e.g. a sugar pill). A typical double-blind study would be as follows. Two groups of patients would typically be used. The groups would, as far as is possible, be equal in the severity of their pain symptoms. Group 1 would receive the drug and Group 2 a placebo. The reactions would be compared. The patients would not know whether they were receiving drug or placebo. The clinical assessors would not know to which group their patients belonged. Both would be 'blind' to what is going on, hence the term 'double-blind'.

The outcome of double-blind studies are crucial for the acceptance and success of a drug. As Wall so succinctly puts it:

> *A satisfactory answer is worth millions of pounds. It takes the question out of the philosophers' conundrum–riddled tutorial onto the floor of the stock exchange. (Wall, 1993, p. 188)*

4.8.2 Some examples of the placebo effect

Wall (1993) discusses the phenomenon of surgical placebo, said by some to be a particularly powerful example. Consider the pain of angina, which is caused by an inadequate supply of blood to the heart muscle. An operation for this condition consisted of tying certain arteries not supplying the heart but running nearby, in the expectation that the disturbance of blood flow dynamics would stimulate a sprouting of new blood vessels through heart muscle. A large number of patients received the operation and many were satisfied with it. However, in spite of the success of the operation, later investigators were unable to find any evidence of such sprouting of new vessels. This prompted a double-blind study into the possibility of a placebo effect.

Stop and think about what is involved in such an investigation. How would you go about performing it? What ethical issues would be raised by such a study?

The experimental group would have the same operation as before. The control group would receive a surgical incision sufficient to reveal the arteries in question and later to give the patient the impression that the full operation had been performed, but no tying of arteries would be made. Both groups would be told that they were receiving an operation involving tying arteries. Neither patients nor their clinicians involved in assessment would know to which group a patient has been allocated. Only other investigators would know this. The ethical problem is of course that, in trying to serve the interests of science, some patients are lied to about what is being done to them. Such an ethical consideration would surely prevent similar studies being performed now. There is also a legal consideration involved. Suppose the patient decided to sue the hospital or the patient died whilst undergoing placebo surgery.

None-the-less, the study was performed (in the USA in the late 1950s) with interesting results (Wall, 1993). Patients in both experimental and control groups reported a significant reduction in pain. The distance that they were able to walk improved and their demand for drugs fell. Even the shape of the electrocardiogram (ECG; see Book 3, Chapter 2) showed an improvement for both groups. The improvement was seen over the six-month observation period that followed the operation.

Another example described by Wall concerned ultrasound therapy applied after extraction of wisdom teeth. This reduces pain and jaw tightness. However, even when the machine was set such as to produce no ultrasound and applied to the skin, there was still an improvement in terms of reduced pain, increased ability to open the mouth and a reduction in swelling. Could it be simply the act of massaging the skin with the apparatus that was effective? Patients were asked to massage their own skin with the apparatus, but no placebo effect was found; Wall suggested:

> *Evidently the therapeutic phenomenon required an impressive machine and someone in a white coat to transmit the effect, even though the emission of ultrasound was not required. (Wall, 1993, p. 189)*

As far as obtaining a placebo effect from chemicals is concerned, capsules made up of coloured beads give a stronger effect than coloured tablets. Round white tablets are relatively ineffective compared to coloured tablets. An intramuscular injection of a placebo substance (e.g. mild saline) is better than any tablet but less effective than an intravenous injection of the same substance (Wall, 1993). The importance that the patient attaches to the procedure seems to be crucial.

It is not difficult to imagine how one might test for a placebo effect of a drug, i.e. by giving neutral tablets that look just like the real drug. To imagine how to conduct a test for a placebo effect in, for example, acupuncture is much more difficult. What would the procedure consist of? Applying needles to the wrong places? Who should conduct the 'treatment'? Someone unskilled in acupuncture? Clearly, both the scientific and ethical dilemmas are enormous.

The placebo effect is powerful and can excite strong emotions, as Wall notes from personal experience:

> *When doctors, who are not involved in a therapy under trial, learn that it turns out to be a placebo, they howl with laughter. When you are the subject in a trial and discover that you have reacted to a placebo, as I have, you feel a fool. When you are the proponent or inventor of a therapy, whether based on contemporary rationale or old-fashioned faith, you are resentful of the need for placebo testing. If the test reveals a substantial placebo component in the response, diversions are created to eliminate consideration of the placebo effect. (Wall, 1993, p. 192)*

Exploiting the placebo effect to a therapeutic end raises a profound ethical issue – to what extent is it right to employ deception? Is the expression 'benevolent lie' (Wall, 1993) ethically justifiable? A related issue concerns the extent to which it is wise even to discuss in the public domain the issue of placebos, including here in this course. Are we robbing medicine of some of its 'magic' and thereby its efficacy? These are complex issues for which we can offer you no simple answers but they are questions you might usefully consider.

4.8.3 Explaining the effect

So how do we explain the placebo response? Researchers have been able to identify at least two factors that play a role: (1) learning through direct past experience of pain relief and (2) an expectancy generated through knowledge, e.g. being told about the effect of a pill (Voudouris *et al.*, 1990). Under some conditions, there might well be some overlap between these two processes. For example, an expectancy might arise partly on the basis of direct experience. However, for some purposes, a distinction can be made between two processes. The emphasis of the first is upon experience and of the second is on knowledge gained without first-hand experience.

The explanation of how learning through experience can play a role is based upon the principles formalized by Pavlov (discussed in Book 3, Chapter 6). In the case of the pain placebo effect, the logic is that most patients have had a history of obtaining relief from certain symptoms when in a context of medical treatment. Important-looking people, often in white coats, inject us or write out prescriptions that relieve our symptoms, e.g. pain. Just as Pavlov's dog came to salivate in response to the bell and before the food actually arrived, so do we start to feel a relief of pain just by means of being exposed to cues which in the past have been paired with relief. Note that for such a process to work there is no need for the subject to understand in any sense (e.g. to be able to articulate consciously the fact) that he or she has formed an association. Indeed, experience plays a role in a placebo pain response in rats as well as in humans. An example that would appear to be open to explanation in these terms is that of cancer patients receiving narcotics at regular intervals (Wall, 1993). If, occasionally, a saline solution is surreptitiously substituted for the narcotic, pain relief is still obtained. The relief follows a similar time course to that derived from the narcotic. The passage of time since the last injection is itself not sufficient to trigger a placebo effect; missing an injection is associated with an increase in pain, whereas the placebo injection causes a decrease.

Concerning the second process, by reading or hearing about pain relief, humans can acquire some knowledge and expectation of the efficacy of analgesics. For example, a doctor might tell the patient that she is prescribing a powerful analgesic. Placebo effects tend to occur when the subject reports having an expectation of obtaining an analgesic effect. The behaviour of the therapist can play powerful and subtle roles here. Whether through direct experience or by cultural learning about pain-reducing effects, it might be expected that children would have less exposure to medical interventions and analgesia than adults. Indeed, the evidence shows that placebos that work for adults tend to be ineffective for 5-year-old children (Wall, 1993). However, the idea that 'Mummy or Daddy will kiss it better' does, apparently, have some efficacy.

These two processes define some of the conditions for a placebo response. How do they work? The process involving a history of associations between a medical context and relief of pain need present no great conceptual hurdle. By comparison, Pavlov's dog came to salivate not only to the bell but also to the presence of experimenters who had been associated with feeding (see Figure 4.8). The brain contains its own intrinsic analgesic system involving opioids, which might, along similar lines, be susceptible to conditioning, though we cannot be sure that it is specifically opioids that are involved in the placebo effect (Wall, 1993). A medical intervention such as a drug would elicit analgesia. A cue that in the past was paired with triggering the analgesic system could come to do so in its own right by its history of association.

The process involving expectations (e.g. simply believing in the efficacy of something by trusting a caring person) is somewhat more difficult to conceptualize. How can knowledge, an expectation, gained from living in a culture in which such things are discussed or just a recently acquired belief cause a physical effect, e.g. the release of, say, opioids? This is a matter of great theoretical interest but as yet little in the way of answers is available. Some of the issues raised by this phenomenon are discussed in the next section.

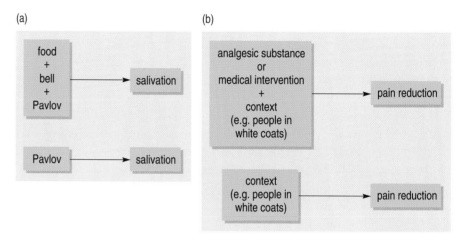

Figure 4.8   How classical conditioning might contribute to the placebo effect: (a) Pavlov's salivary conditioning situation; (b) analgesia. First, specific interventions create analgesia. Then, by Pavlovian conditioning, the context in which this occurred can, on its own, produce some analgesia.

4.8.4 The mind–body problem

Wall (1993, p. 192) rejects absolutely as 'the most dangerous and cruel attitude', the argument that has been advanced in some medical quarters that the placebo effect can distinguish between organic and mental disease. In such terms, it is only the mental component of a disorder, or a mentally disturbed type of patient, who would be expected to react to a placebo. Wall notes the hundreds of scientific studies showing a placebo response in patients suffering pain from organically diagnosed disorder. Although there can be wide differences between individuals, there is no obvious placebo-prone personality type (Wall, 1993).

Consideration of the placebo takes us to the heart of a philosophical dilemma that has troubled the study of behaviour for a very long time. This is the issue of the **mind–body problem** (Campbell, 1994), i.e. how should we conceptualize the dependence between mind and body? Campbell notes that the implicit assumption behind most medical writing is a so-called materialist interpretation of mental phenomena. That is to say, the mental phenomena are absolutely dependent upon the physical brain for their existence. However, the way that the placebo effect is commonly discussed in medicine implies a belief in a fundamental mind–brain duality, in spite of the same culture's explicit or implicit objections to such duality. Campbell writes:

There is thus a temptation to say, in effect, that there is the body, which is a physiological system on which drugs and other medical treatments are supposed to operate, and there is the mind, which can be affected by suggestion to produce a spurious effect. Between the mind and the body there is an ill-defined no-man's land rather inadequately occupied by something called psychosomatic medicine. It seems difficult to talk about placebos without implying a dualistic model of this kind. (Campbell, 1994)

Campbell suggests an interpretation based upon the following assumptions:

1   Pain is a product of the physical brain.

2   Pain reduction, whether by direct pharmacological intervention or by placebo effects, can only be effected via the physical brain.

3   Procedures such as acupuncture, taking placebo tablets or being in a certain 'state of mind' must correspond to an alteration of the physical activity of the brain.

The duality that Campbell sees pervading medicine is relevant to earlier sections of this chapter. Thus, in the context of intractable back pain, he considers the situation where investigations could find no structural abnormalities that might account for the pain. In such cases, the pain was usually described as 'functional'. Campbell suggests that this was just 'a polite way of saying that it was psychological and therefore not "real"'.

Although thinking amongst specialists has changed, a number of doctors still draw a distinction between 'functional' pain and 'real' pain. Campbell refers to a phenomenon termed *somatization*, in which patients experience their state of depression or unhappiness in terms of a reported physical pain and adds:

Many doctors find such patients irritating and difficult to cope with. No doubt they should not, but they do, and they tend to think that pain of this kind is somehow less deserving of sympathy than pain that is obviously due to a physical disease. (Campbell, 1994)

Campbell goes on to argue that the distinction is illogical since any pain is real. Only the processes that underlie it are different. In such terms, the notion that drugs exert a real effect whereas the placebo is 'merely psychological' is an equally invalid dichotomy.

Summary of Section 4.8

1   The placebo effect can be explained by two processes: (a) Pavlovian conditioning based upon experience of analgesia and (b) expectations and beliefs about the efficacy of a process.

2   In the context of pain relief, placebos contribute towards an analgesic effect.

3   The phenomenon of the placebo effect calls for an integrated view of mind and body.

4.9 Hypnosis

Discussion of the placebo effect might also be able to illuminate other phenomena. For example, an issue of some controversy in pain research is the status of hypnosis. As Gracely (1994) points out, the study of this labours under a double burden. Pain is subjective and not open to quantitative measurement, whereas the hypnotic treatment itself cannot be described in the terms of conventional medicine and quantified.

There are various explanatory models for hypnosis, one of which suggests that there is no effect beyond a kind of labelling process. In these terms, subjects interpret their state as special and simply act according to their perceived expectations of how a hypnotized person is expected to behave. If this were the case in pain relief, one might suggest that the pain is no less but patients conform to the social expectation in reporting a reduction. It is difficult to test such ideas in any kind of formal way. However, suppose hypnosis really taps into a specific pain pathway. Is there some behavioural measure that could be employed to index this? Recently Kiernan *et al.* (1995) claimed to have found just such an index. They looked at a spinal reflex of limb movement stimulated by a noxious stimulus applied to an ankle. The magnitude of this reflex was reduced by hypnosis. This suggests that the hypnotic state was effective in triggering a pathway of descending inhibition that opposed the signals in the nociceptive neurons. Thus the experiment suggests that reports of a reduction in pain as a result of hypnosis do reflect something specific to pain rather than simply being a social conformity effect.

Summary of Section 4.9

1   Some patients derive an analgesic effect from hypnosis.

2   There is evidence that hypnosis can lower the reactivity of some spinal nociceptive reflexes.

4.10 Pain relief – a socio-political controversy

Ronald Melzack made a provocative presidential address to the Fifth World Congress on Pain, entitled 'The tragedy of needless pain: a call for social action' (Melzack, 1988). In this address, Melzack argued that many people are being denied treatment for their pains on the grounds that they might become addicted to the agent used in the treatment. He suggests that such fears are unfounded and represent dogma rather than science.

Melzack starts by noting that there are a wide range of pains for which we cannot provide effective therapy, simply because we do not have the scientific knowledge necessary. However, there are other pains for which we do have the means available to combat but are reluctant to do so. Melzack offers a personal anecdote to make the point:

My brother-in-law, whom I loved very much, had cancer and died in terrible pain. For months he suffered not only pain but something just as frightening – the loss of his personal dignity by having to weep and plead for the next injection of morphine. (Melzack, 1988)

Melzack's brother-in-law was allowed only small amounts of morphine, since his doctor believed that if he was given larger amounts he would develop tolerance (a decreasing effectiveness of the drug). This would mean that, as the pain got worse nearer the end, he would be undefended. Melzack claims that this fear was groundless, and that the evidence is overwhelming that neither a major tolerance nor addiction usually occur when narcotics are administered for the relief of pain.

Melzack reports that in spite of such evidence, world-wide millions of people continue to die in needless pain. He suggests that the reason is simple: there is a sweeping generalization made from the so-called street addict to the patient in pain. This generalization is spread by misinformation in medical and nursing schools and by confusion on the part of law enforcement agencies. Much of this is on the grounds that to prescribe morphine is to create street addicts. Children fare particularly badly in being denied help. Whereas morphine can either abolish, or almost abolish, the pain of cancer in some 80–90% of patients, it is unavailable to large numbers of them, in spite of a WHO recommendation for its use. Yet Melzack presents the evidence from controlled studies showing that patients can be maintained on morphine for months or even years without developing tolerance. Commonly successful treatment is followed by the patient herself or himself requesting that the dose be reduced, but without any withdrawal effects being shown.

Melzack claims that the bases of why people require and request morphine are quite different comparing addicts and people in pain, explaining the former in terms of psychological sickness. Psychologically healthy people simply tend not to become addicts when exposed to narcotics. In one survey cited by Melzack, of 11 882 patients treated, all without a history of drug abuse, only four showed evidence of later abuse and in only one of the four was it considered to be major. Similarly, amongst the many thousands of Israeli military casualties of the Yom Kippur war, there was not one case of addiction subsequently reported.

On theoretical grounds, the case can be made even stronger than that presented by Melzack, and principles of motivation used to support it. Thus, the craving for opioid drugs, even amongst so-called street addicts, is very much a function of the addict's present environment. If this is changed, then the craving commonly falls. Craving is particularly potent in a context in which the addict took the drug in the past, and this appears to reflect a process of Pavlovian conditioning.

The presence of familiar cues such as other addicts and a hypodermic syringe, which in the past were associated with the effects of the drug, serve to prime the motivational system. Memories of past 'highs' are revived. A large number of US military personnel in Vietnam took heroin, it being relatively easily available. It was expected that at the end of the war when they returned home, they would take a major problem with them, but this was simply not the case. Most became reintegrated into society without a heroin problem. Bearing in mind the environmental factors playing a role in drug taking, it is clear that there is a vast difference in context between being in pain in a hospital and being free of pain at home. The kind of memories of the drug that might be revived would be entirely different from those of the addict.

Quite apart from the dubious risks of tolerance and addiction, we know that chronic pain has serious consequences that are to the detriment of the patient. Post-surgical pain can hinder the circulation necessary to supply nutrients and oxygen to the affected tissue (Melzack, 1988). Pain can trigger the stress system (see Chapter 5), cause the release of corticosteroids and thereby inhibit the immune system.

Melzack concludes his presidential address to the congress with an urge to do battle against 'misinformation, ignorance and needless suffering'.

Summary of Section 4.10

1   Many patients are denied access to opioid analgesics on the grounds of fear of addiction.

2   The evidence suggests that there is little risk of addiction in administering opioids to patients for relief of chronic pain.

4.11   Conclusions

To some extent we can gain considerable understanding of pain by looking at (1) activity in peripheral processes, i.e. small- and large-diameter fibres and (2) connections made within the spinal cord. For example, much of analgesia can be understood by looking at this part of the system. However, there are limits to how far we can go towards understanding pain by looking at such factors.

You might have felt that pain was not an obvious candidate for understanding in holistic terms. It might have seemed fairly straight-forward, with tissue damage as the necessary and sufficient condition to trigger a pain reaction. Indeed, since Descartes, the favourite model of pain has been in terms of such a straight-through transmission of information. Doubtless, in spite of the Melzack/Wall model, there are many who still think in these terms. In such terms, phenomena such as: (1) phantom-limb pain, (2) placebo effects, (3) tissue damage but no pain and (4) pain in the absence of tissue damage, are odd phenomena that don't really fit anywhere. To consider them at all, requires resort to a dualistic model of mind–brain and often banishment of the patients to the psychiatry department. In such terms, patients complaining of pain but showing no obvious sign of organic damage must be fundamentally different from 'real patients'.

A broader approach, as taken here, involves looking at the sensory input side, considering the gate theory and the active participation of the brain in the construction of sensation and experience. This then gives a basis for considering a wider range of phenomena within a single integrative framework. This framework requires an understanding of neurons and how the nervous system works. It also requires an integration of this knowledge with that from psychology. The brain is seen as playing an active role in the generation of conscious experience, including that of a 'self'. It is assumed that there are neural pathways within the brain that are active at a time corresponding to the pain sensation. These pathways can be triggered by noxious input. However, they are not always dependent upon such input for their activation. They can also be excited under circumstances where appropriate noxious input is not present, as in the phantom limb phenomenon.

Analgesics such as morphine act to counter the input to these pain neural circuits in the brain. We know at least some of the sites of the action of morphine at the spinal cord and in the brain. Under some circumstances, there can be an analgesic effect even in the absence of applying analgesic substances, the so-called placebo effect. This effect has something in common with phantom pain. In each case, it would seem that the level of activation of the pain neural circuits in the brain fails to reflect afferent input. Apparently, in the phantom effects there is activation without afferent input and in the placebo effect there is a reduction in activation without reduction in afferent input.

Objectives for Chapter 4

After reading this chapter, you should be able to:

4.1 Define and use, or recognize definitions and applications of, each of the terms printed in **bold** in the text.

4.2 Explain what is the significance for pain of the terms 'nociceptor', 'nociceptive neuron' and 'large-diameter fibre', by relating these terms to each other. (*Questions 4.1 and 4.2*)

4.3 Explain why we no longer believe that pain is always related to tissue damage in a simple one-to-one way. (*Questions 4.1 and 4.2*)

4.4 Describe the gate theory of pain. (*Question 4.2*)

4.5 Describe what is meant by 'referred pain' and propose how it might be explained. (*Question 4.3*)

4.6 Explain the action of analgesics that act at different sites. (*Questions 4.3 and 4.4*)

4.7 Describe what is meant by phantom limb pain and its implications for theories of pain. (*Question 4.5*)

4.8 Explain what is meant by the term 'placebo effect' and what are its implications for understanding pain. (*Questions 4.6 and 4.7*)

Questions for Chapter 4

Question 4.1 *(Objective 4.2)*

Why is it misleading to use the terms 'nociceptor' and 'pain receptor' synonymously?

Question 4.2 *(Objectives 4.2, 4.3 and 4.4)*

Sufferers from hay-fever commonly rub their eyes in summer. Is it possible to provide any rationale for this behaviour? What does this suggest about gates at spinal and non-spinal locations?

Question 4.3 *(Objectives 4.5 and 4.6)*

With reference to the situation of tissue damage at the heart, discussed in Section 4.5 and illustrated in Figure 4.5, why would Lignocaine be an inappropriate medication?

Question 4.4 *(Objective 4.6)*

Examine Figure 4.4. Injection of the following would be expected to lead to either: (a) pain or (b) analgesia in response to an otherwise painful stimulus. Which is which?

1   An agonist to substance P.

2   An agonist to enkephalins.

Question 4.5 *(Objectives 4.7)*

In the phenomenon of a phantom limb, what is the evidence that sensory information arising from both nociceptors and detectors of innocuous stimuli can be held in memory and later enter consciousness even in the absence of the appropriate sensory stimulation?

Question 4.6 *(Objective 4.8)*

According to the processes proposed to underlie the placebo effect, how might an otherwise effective placebo lose its efficacy? (Note in Pavlov's salivary conditioning experiment, the bell will lose its efficacy to cause salivation if it is repeatedly presented in the absence of food.)

Question 4.7 *(Objective 4.8)*

Two researchers are having a discussion. Dr X suggests that she has discovered a new analgesic. Dr Y is more sceptical and he argues that 'the reaction is no stronger than that observed when using a placebo'. What might be meant by such a claim? What would constitute a rigorous experiment to decide the issue?

References

Campbell, A. (1994) Cartesian dualism and the concept of medical placebos, *Journal of Consciousness Studies*, **1**, 230–233.

Filshie, J. and Morrison, P. J. (1988) Acupuncture for chronic pain: a review, *Palliative Medicine*, **2**, 1–14.

Gracely, R. H. (1995) Hypnosis and hierarchical pain control systems, *Pain*, **60**, 1–2.

Kiernan, B. D., Dane, J. R., Phillips, L. H. and Price, D. D. (1995) Hypnotic analgesia reduces R-III nociceptive reflex: further evidence concerning the multifactorial nature of hypnotic analgesia, *Pain*, **60**, 39–47.

Melzack, R. (1988) The tragedy of needless pain: a call for social action, in R. Dubner, G. F. Gubner and M. R. Bond (eds) *Proceedings of the Vth World Congress on Pain*, pp. 1–11, Elsevier Science Publishers, Amsterdam.

Melzack, R. (1989) Phantom limbs, the self and the brain (The D. O. Hebb memorial lecture), *Canadian Psychology*, **30**, 1–16.

Melzack, R. (1993) Pain: past, present and future, *Canadian Journal of Experimental Psychology*, **47**, 615–629.

Melzack, R and Wall, P. D. (1982) *The Challenge of Pain*, Penguin Books, Harmondsworth.

Voudouris, N. J., Peck, C. L. and Coleman, G. (1990) The role of conditioning and verbal expectancy in the placebo response, *Pain*, **43**, 121–128.

Wall, P. (1993) Pain and the placebo response, in G. R. Bock and J. Marsh (eds) *Experimental and Theoretical Studies of Consciousness – CIBA Foundation Symposium*, no. 174, Wiley, Chichester.

CHAPTER 5
EMOTIONAL HEALTH AND STRESS

5.1 Introduction

We begin this chapter by asking you to reflect for a moment on some significant events in your own life and the emotions that you experienced then. Probably both happy and sad times will readily spring to mind. There will have been (1) emotional 'gut feelings' (the expression is very apt) of relaxation, euphoria, 'sinking' or tension and (2) specific thought processes of achievement or failure, warmth towards others or hostility. You might recall that as part of some of these experiences your digestive tract was functioning in a disturbed way. Just a moment's reflection will reveal how the various aspects of a complex system of emotion work as an integrated whole; specific thoughts ('cognitions'), subjectively felt emotions and bodily manifestations are all inextricably linked. As you learnt in Book 2, Chapter 5, emotional state can also influence the activity of the immune system.

Of course, emotions, both positive and negative, are an inevitable part of everyday life. However, we have some measure of freedom and so may be able to organize our lives such as to tilt the balance of activity of this whole complex system in favour of the positive emotions. Much of the negative side of emotion that we experience these days is described as **stress**, yet the term proves difficult to define in a rigorous way. Some might argue that stress is always bad and is virtually synonymous with certain forms of pathology. Others would assert that stress is a normal part of living and that we should be concerned only when it becomes excessive. Much of the literature agrees on the idea that in some way perfectly adaptive behavioural mechanisms (e.g. acceleration of heart rate at times of emergency) can be stretched to beyond their adaptive range of functioning (Toates, 1995). In such terms, stress represents a long-term failure of coping mechanisms to function optimally. However, we can sometimes exert at least some agency over the events that otherwise cause stress in our lives.

Our environment presents us with **stressors**, i.e. stress-inducing agents or situations, such as confrontation with a charging bull or, perhaps more likely these days, the challenge of driving in heavy traffic or the chronic fear of financial insecurity. In response to some such stressors, we are able to recruit various defence mechanisms (e.g. running away) that have functioned rather well in our evolutionary history. We thus have particular coping mechanisms. However, if, in the absence of the appropriate coping mechanisms, we are stretched by the stressors too much and over long periods of time, then pathological stress can result.

pathological

We associate such stress with certain types of illness (e.g. gastric ulcers, irritable bowel syndrome, coronary heart disease, insomnia) whose causes lie in our interaction with both the physical and social environment. However, sometimes stress can not only be managed but one can have a healthy reactivity of those systems which would be malfunctioning in stress. What in stress is a pathology-inducing threat, might actually be welcomed as a life challenge. Of course, much depends upon the nature of our social context and how we are able to react within it.

Stress and its correction involve both the voluntary and the autonomic nervous systems; interventions to counter stress can target either. The voluntary nervous system is involved in that we might have some choice over the courses of action we pursue in life and how we construe and react to the events we experience. For example, we have some control over those aspects of our interpersonal relations that generate hostility. We might choose to behave differently, albeit with some difficulty and with the need of help. The autonomic nervous system is involved in that stressors tend to trigger activity in this system (causing, for example, pounding of the heart, increased gut motility).

Section 5.2 looks at some of the basic physiology that is most obviously associated with emotional health and stress. Then, in Section 5.3, we consider some features of lifestyle that appear to contribute positively to emotional health. Section 5.4 is concerned with stress and personality. We look at how stress arises, how it can be challenged and how the mechanisms that underlie stress might be harnessed to one's benefit. Section 5.5 looks briefly at the relationships between the nervous, endocrine and immune systems.

Summary of Section 5.1

1   The different aspects of emotion work as an integrated whole, i.e. specific thoughts ('cognitions'), subjectively felt emotions and bodily reactions are all inextricably linked. Emotion is linked with the activity of the immune system.

2   Stress might be defined as a state induced by stressors in which there is a chronic stretching of coping mechanisms to beyond their optimal range.

5.2 Basic physiology of emotion

Not surprisingly, emotions are associated with a wide variety of physiological changes throughout the body. We have already described, at a number of points in the course, some of these physiological events. Therefore most of this section should serve as revision for you.

There are two major systems that have traditionally been associated with emotion. One of these is the autonomic nervous system, ANS (Book 2, Chapter 3). The ANS has two branches.

❑   What are these called?

◼   The sympathetic and parasympathetic branches.

The sympathetic branch of the ANS is excited mainly (though not exclusively) in times of emergency and causes such things as an increased heart rate and ventilation rate. The parasympathetic branch, on the other hand, is concerned with maintaining the resting state of the body's internal organs and promoting such involuntary processes as gut motility and the production of digestive secretions.

The sympathetic nervous system exerts its effects through the release of (a) noradrenalin from the terminals of sympathetic neurons themselves and (b) adrenalin and noradrenalin from the adrenal glands (Figure 5.1) in response to activity in the sympathetic neurons that innervate these glands.

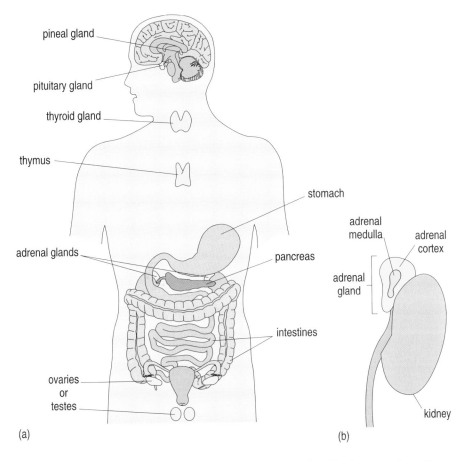

Figure 5.1   The adrenal glands: (a) location in the body; (b) close-up view of one gland showing the division into adrenal medulla and adrenal cortex.

Noradrenalin and adrenalin activate two different types of receptor at various sites in the body, termed alpha adrenergic and beta adrenergic receptors. (The separation into two categories was originally on the basis of their sensitivities to certain drugs – remember the alpha adrenergic action of nicotine mentioned in Chapter 3 – but there is an important

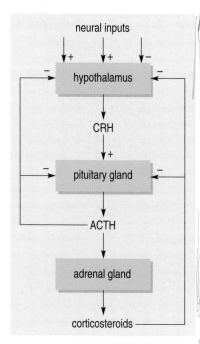

Figure 5.2 The brain's control over the secretion of cortico-steroids. CRH from the hypothalamus triggers the release of ACTH from the pituitary gland. ACTH stimulates the secretion of corticosteroids by the adrenal glands.

physiological distinction too.) Beta adrenergic receptors are present on the heart muscle cells and one effect of occupation of these receptors is to increase the heart rate and strength of contraction. The effect of noradrenalin from the terminals of sympathetic neurons is reinforced by noradrenalin and adrenalin arriving from the adrenal glands via the bloodstream. Both substances attach themselves to the beta receptors on the heart muscle. The effect can be such as to increase the cardiac output by a factor of five. Adrenalin and noradrenalin also bind to beta adrenergic receptors in the walls of the coronary arteries that supply blood to the heart muscle, causing these arteries to dilate, thus facilitating an increased flow of blood through them, enhancing the supply of blood (and hence nutrients and oxygen) to the heart muscle. The same effect at the beta adrenergic receptors in the walls of the arteries to the skeletal muscles serves to increase the amount of blood entering these muscles too. (You will recall from Chapter 3 that activation of *alpha* adrenergic receptors in artery walls – in the penis, for example – results in the opposite effect, i.e. vasoconstriction.)

The adrenal glands are also responsible for the secretion of a class of hormones known as **corticosteroids**. These are steroid hormones that are released specifically from the outer region of the gland, known as the **adrenal cortex** (see Figure 5.1). Corticosteroids play a variety of roles throughout the body, one of which (as you learnt in Book 3, Chapter 4) is to stimulate the production and mobilization of nutrients for use in an emergency. In humans, the principal corticosteroid is cortisol.

The control of the secretion of corticosteroids is summarized in Figure 5.2. As illustrated in Figure 5.3, there are neurons in the brain that secrete a hormone called corticotropin-releasing hormone (CRH). This hormone is then carried in special local blood vessels a short distance to the pituitary gland where it exerts its action. Emotional stress act as a trigger for CRH release.

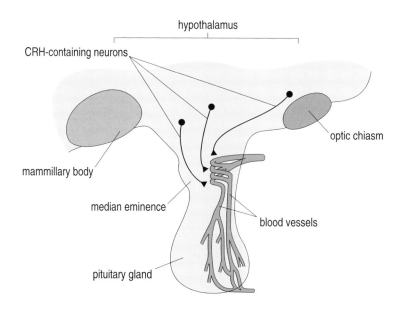

Figure 5.3 The release of CRH and its transport to the pituitary gland. Note the local blood supply which transports CRH from the hypothalamus to the pituitary gland.

CRH stimulates the release of adrenocorticotropic hormone (ACTH) from the pituitary gland. ACTH is then carried in the bloodstream to the outer layer (cortex) of the adrenal gland (see Figure 5.1), where it stimulates the release of corticosteroids. The sequence CRH → ACTH → corticosteroids is termed the **pituitary adrenocortical system**. The fact that activity in the hypothalamus is the trigger for CRH secretion is sometimes used to give this system the still more daunting title of *hypothalamic pituitary adrenocortical system*. Note in Figure 5.2 the negative feedback effect of corticosteroids; they tend to inhibit their own secretion. As mentioned in Book 2, Chapter 5, and discussed later in the present chapter, one effect of corticosteroids is to depress the activity of the immune system. The biological significance of this is still something of a mystery, but it is an effect that is of importance in understanding how stress influences the normal functioning of the body.

If one is confronted with a charging bull or faced with a similar emergency requiring a 'fight or flight' response, the activities of the sympathetic nervous system (e.g. exciting the heart to beat faster and more strongly and increasing the blood supply to both cardiac and skeletal muscle) and of the pituitary adrenocortical system (e.g. promoting the release of glucose and fatty acids into the bloodstream) are clearly adaptive. Once across the fence to the safety of the other side, these systems would normally return to their baseline levels. The danger comes when these systems are excited in a way that is inappropriate for the behaviour that occurs. A classic situation here is that of exciting these systems over long periods of time whilst in a sedentary situation, e.g. sitting at a desk all day doing a stressful job.

It is found that blood lipid levels are an important indicator for stress or emotional health. Lipids tend to accumulate on the walls of arteries, a phenomenon termed atherosclerosis (discussed in Book 3, Chapter 2, as well as Chapter 3 of the present book); the factors that affect this process are of crucial interest to us. Two such lipids, triacylglycerols and cholesterol, are particularly important (Johnsgard, 1989). These substances are transported in the bloodstream in association with proteins, the combination being termed a lipoprotein (Book 3, Chapter 4). A chronic elevation of lipid levels, particularly where they remain unmetabolized as in inactivity, is a risk to the health of the circulatory system. This situation occurs during stress.

Finally, we need to consider the immune system. Traditionally, the immune system would have been described somewhat in isolation from other systems. However, in recent years there has been a growing awareness that the nervous, endocrine and immune systems of the body interact with each other in complex ways, and this was reflected in the approach adopted in Book 2, Chapter 5. A disturbance in any of these three systems can have an influence on the other two. In this chapter, since, as far as we know, emotions and stress arise in the central nervous system, we are particularly concerned with effects of the nervous system upon the immune system. Some of these effects are mediated directly and others are mediated via hormones.

It has long been known that corticosteroids influence the immune system. A rise in corticosteroid level tends to suppress the immune system. Thus stressors, which increase the levels of corticosteroids, can have a negative effect upon the immune system.

Summary of Section 5.2

1   Emotional states are associated with a variety of physiological changes throughout the body. There are some well recognized changes that have traditionally been seen as the indices of emotional states.

2   Stress tends to be associated with activation of the sympathetic nervous system.

3   Stress activates the pituitary adrenocortical system.

4   Chronic stress is associated with lipid deposition on the walls of the arteries (atherosclerosis).

5   There are reciprocal links from both the nervous and the endocrine systems to the immune system. Corticosteroids can exert an inhibitory effect upon the immune system.

5.3 Some factors contributing to emotional health

5.3.1 Introduction

This section considers three aspects of life that can contribute to emotional health. It is not simply that they might help to prevent or cure physiological and emotional disorders but rather that they can help achieve a state of emotional health. One of these, physical exercise, involves large measurable changes in the physiology of the body. The other two, a sense of belonging and pet ownership, are more subtle inputs.

5.3.2 Social interactions and emotional health

Introduction

There is a growing recognition that social interactions have significant effects on emotional well-being. Such interactions can sometimes be characterized by the term **belonging**. By 'belonging' we mean living a life in interaction with others in such a way that the individual has a purpose, a common goal to which he or she can strive in social interaction and feel part of an harmonious network of relationships. The individual is able to attain 'social goals' (i.e. has some capacity for prediction, control and coping) by positive means rather than by threat or cohesion. As part of his/her life, the belonging person is able to react in response to positive incentives and is not subject to undue threats.

Belonging can be attained within either a family or some other grouping with shared ideals, such as a church. It has long been known that there is a relationship between one's social circle and one's health. In terms of a wide variety of disorders, the socially isolated are at greater risk than those who are socially integrated in an harmonious way (House, Landis and Umberson, 1988; Williams, 1995). It has not always been possible to identify what is cause and effect but recently epidemiological analyses have shown beyond all doubt the importance of the social factor.

Religious and cultural factors

Amongst Israelis, the incidence of myocardial infarction (heart attack) is much greater in secular subjects than in religious orthodox subjects. Why is this? In males, the concentration of high density lipoproteins (HDL) in the blood showed a negative correlation with the frequency of myocardial infarction (Friedlander, Kark and Stein, 1986). Recall from Book 3, Chapter 4, that cholesterol is present in the bloodstream in both HDL and LDL (low density lipoproteins) and that the LDL/HDL ratio is thought to be the best indicator of the risk of atherosclerosis; the higher this ratio, the greater the risk. Could there be differences in LDL/HDL ratios between secular and religious subjects that might explain the difference in incidence of myocardial infarction? Pointing in this direction, a study of 17-year-old Jewish residents of Jerusalem (Friedlander *et al.*, 1987) found higher blood levels of LDL in secular young people than the religious orthodox group.

Suppose that a difference in LDL/HDL ratio is the crucial factor in explaining the different incidence of myocardial infarction between religious and secular subjects. In turn, how might the difference in this ratio be explained? Such lifestyle factors as healthier eating and lower alcohol and cigarette consumption amongst the religious subjects would be expected to play a role. However, the authors suggested that these factors could not explain all of the effect. Friedlander *et al.* (1986) write:

> *Psychosocial factors could play a protective role in the religious groups. Orthodox religious Jews are generally characterized by the social cohesiveness and strong social supports of their traditional culture. The extreme religious community is less exposed to cultural change and their way of life is characterized by a traditional orientation generally unchallenged from within the community.*

On the basis of the strength of the effect, they suggest:

> *…that religious orthodoxy may be an important independent protective factor for the development of myocardial infarction in the Israeli population.*

Of the industrialized countries, Japan has one of the lowest mortality rates from coronary heart disease whereas the United States has one of the highest (Marmot and Syme, 1976). Interestingly, compared to Japanese people living in Japan, those living in California were found to have a much higher rate, and those in Hawaii an intermediate rate. Within California, Japanese males who had become assimilated into an American way of life had a higher frequency of coronary heart disease (by a factor of five) and cardiac abnormalities (as revealed by electrocardiogram, ECG, recordings) than those who retained a traditional culture. The most integrated were comparable to Caucasian Americans and the least integrated comparable to Japanese living in Japan. Differences in diet and incidence of smoking appear to explain only a part of the effect. Even when Japanese males eating a similar diet in Japan or California are compared, those in California had higher blood cholesterol levels. Research suggests that cultural factors play an important role. In traditional Japanese culture, a heavy premium is placed upon social stability, group cohesion and collective achievement. By contrast, as Marmot and Syme (p. 246) note, American and Northern European cultures:

> …*display almost opposite characteristics to the protective features described, i.e. lack of stability, accent on the individual rather than the group, and a high likelihood of an individual finding himself in a situation for which his world-view has left him unprepared.*

A similar protective effect of a close-knit community has been found in traditional Italian communities living in Pennsylvania (Bovard, 1985).

A study of elderly patients recovering from major cardiac surgery (typically, a bypass operation for atherosclerosis of coronary arteries) was carried out recently in New England (Oxman, Freman and Manheimer, 1995). Length of survival was greatly increased in patients who reported participation in group activities and the comfort of religious belief. As far as the authors could ascertain, the effect was not simply mediated via an association of the kind that religious belief is correlated negatively with smoking or positively with having a partner around. The authors suggested that:

> …*physicians may eventually be advised to make relatively simple inquiries about and reinforcement of group participation and religious involvement as routinely as they inquire and advise about cigarette smoking and hypertension.*

Explaining the health benefits of belonging

How might we start to explain the effects of positive social bonds upon health? In seeking an explanation, religion might be seen as a kind of social bond, albeit in part with an invisible non-human being. It also involves social bonds with other followers. There are various theories of how social contact can mediate effects upon the body and health (Bovard, 1985; Williams, 1995). Such theories embrace the idea that we have evolved within a social matrix. We come into the world utterly dependent upon other human beings for support. Therefore, there is every reason to believe that, underlying social interaction, there exist specific brain processes the organization of which is partly genetically determined but which undergo refinement in response to early environmental factors. Such processes might be expected to play a part in seeking and maintaining social relationships, much as other processes organize the seeking of food or water.

There is evidence that a caring, confident social bond serves as a major buffer against the stresses and strains of life. There are animal models which show that the effects of experimentally induced stressors in causing hypertension, gastric and duodenal ulcers and other disorders are less in the presence of a known member of the same species. In humans, the rise in fatty acid levels in the bloodstream that occurs in response to a stressor (a consequence of elevated activity in both the sympathetic nervous system and the pituitary adrenocortical system) is smaller if a familiar other person is present (Bovard, 1985). Based upon such evidence, Bovard suggests that the presence of family or friends moderates or inhibits sympathetic nervous stimulation (for example, to the heart) and this might be responsible for the improved health of people in family bonds and close-knit communities. Thus the social bonds might provide a natural equivalent of the drugs termed **beta-blockers** in reducing the sympathetic activation of the heart. Beta-blockers occupy the beta receptors at the heart muscle that would normally be occupied by noradrenalin and adrenalin and are antagonistic in their action (Section 5.2).

In situations where social bonds exist, the coronary arteries would also receive less sympathetic activation. A combination of effects upon heart muscle, coronary arteries and fatty acid levels, would all act in the same direction as protection against atherosclerosis. In a hospital context, the establishment of trusting relations (e.g. meeting the anaesthetist and surgeon the day prior to an operation) might help to inhibit excessive sympathetic input to the heart as the operation nears.

How can a purely social contact (e.g. just being with good friends) come to elicit effects within the physiology of the body? Bovard suggests a role for conditioning (see Book 3, Chapter 6). From the moment of birth, the presence of others would be associated with direct positive effects upon the body in the form of nutrients from the breast, warmth and tactile stimulation. Friendly others will be associated with the bringing of such good things. Later, simply the presence of friendly people might on its own be able to exert similar effects. Based upon analogy with animal experiments (Bovard, 1985), there is reason to believe that these effects can be quite subtle. An environment associated with peaceful emotions might acquire the capacity on its own to induce restraint of the sympathetic system. Consider the opposite situation of sympathetic activation in response to aversive events in a particular context (e.g. domestic violence or disharmony). This might mean that Pavlovian conditioning can occur so that the environment in which this was experienced can on its own later come to induce sympathetic activation.

There is an animal experiment to illustrate the role of conditioning that might be relevant to the situation in humans. It was found that petting of a dog by a human reduced the dog's resting heart rate by between 10 and 60 beats per minute. Later it was found that the mere presence of the person who earlier had petted the dog also caused some reduction in heart rate, suggesting a role for Pavlovian conditioning.

In addition to such effects mediated via the autonomic nervous system, it appears that, acting through brain processes, social contact exerts other effects upon the hormonal profile of the body; there is an stimulation of growth hormone production and inhibition of the release of ACTH (Bovard, 1985).

❑   What would you expect to be one effect of a reduction in the rate of ACTH secretion?

■   A lower rate of secretion of corticosteroids.

It appears that the suppression of ACTH and thereby corticosteroid secretion has a dampening effect on the reactivity of the sympathetic branch of the autonomic nervous system.

Effects of emotional stress on growth

Emotional stress suppresses growth hormone secretion and stimulates ACTH secretion. The combination of elevated corticosteroid levels and decreased levels of growth hormone would be expected to lead to decreased growth. The role of such hormones can be illustrated by considering children from severely emotionally disturbed environments (Bovard, 1985; also Book 2, Chapter 2). They commonly exhibit abnormally low weight gain and retardation of bone growth, a condition described as *psychosocial* (or *deprivation*) *dwarfism*. They have abnormally low levels of growth hormone in the blood and high blood levels of ACTH. When such children are removed from the stressful environment, growth rate increases without hormonal supplements.

Some important early developmental effects could be at work here (Bovard, 1985). There is evidence to suggest that growth hormone tends to increase rates of cell division and differentiation and also increases cell size in fetal tissue, whereas corticosteroids exert the opposite effects. Suppose that these two hormones are able to pass from the mother's blood to that of the fetus.

Try to think what would be the implications of this for the relationship between the mother's lifestyle and the baby's development.

Emotional support for the mother could be to the benefit of the fetus, whereas lack of support and social stress could slow fetal growth and development. (In rats, recent evidence shows such a passage of corticosteroids from mother to offspring, and it is very likely that a similar transfer occurs in humans too.)

Researchers have investigated premature infants whose mothers spent a period of one hour per day giving them tactile stimulation and cuddling them over a period of one month after the birth, and compared them to

babies who did not receive such treatment. Compared to the controls, the
stimulated babies had an increased weight gain, more rapidly triggered
reflexes and an increased cognitive development (Bovard, 1985). This is not
altogether surprising; a very similar effect has been found in rat pups given
a comparable tactile treatment. This effect is mediated in part by growth
hormone and in part by the effect of tactile stimulation in biasing the
autonomic nervous system in favour of activity in the parasympathetic
branch and away from activity in the sympathetic branch.

To achieve the healing of a wound or a bone fracture, one can see that there
could be value in trying to reduce stress levels (Bovard, 1985), given that
there can be an antagonistic effect of corticosteroids on healing. The
presence of, for example, a supportive doctor or nurse could help to reduce
activation of the pituitary adrenocortical system and maximize growth
hormone release, which would benefit the healing process.

The relevance of emotional stress to cancer

Researchers have shown that social harmony can have a protective effect
against cancer (Bovard, 1985). However, the magnitude of this effect
should not be exaggerated. Cancer patients with social support have an
increased survival time. The mechanism for this is believed to be an
interaction between psychological state and the functioning of the immune
system (see Section 5.6) mediated, at least in part, by inhibition exerted on
the pituitary adrenocortical system.

❏   How might a reduction in the activity of this system offer protection
      against cancer?

■   Corticosteroids depress activity in the immune system. The immune
      system has a role in limiting the proliferation of cancerous cells.

Having considered the role of social support and harmony in reducing the
adverse effects of emotional stress on health, the following section looks
briefly at whether any such benefits might derive from non-human social
contact.

5.3.3 Pet ownership

There is evidence that pet ownership is good for one's health. Possibly the
pet could fit into the kind of processes underlying social bonds that were
described in the last section. In a study carried out amongst elderly people
living in California, it was found that the number of times a doctor was
called out was smaller amongst pet owners than amongst controls (Siegel,
1990). Attachment to a pet was positively correlated with better mental
health.

James Serpell (1991) of the Companion Animal Research Group at the
University of Cambridge carried out a survey on the effects of acquiring a
pet. In the months following pet acquisition, there were significantly fewer

minor ailments. Although increased physical activity, in the form of walking a dog, probably played some role, it appeared not to be responsible for all of the benefits. A similar study carried out in Melbourne, Australia, looked at the relationship between ownership of a pet and the risk factors for cardiovascular disease (Anderson, Reid and Jennings, 1992). It was found that, in the pet owning group, systolic blood pressure and blood triacylglycerol and cholesterol levels were modestly but significantly lower than amongst those without pets. Again, before it can be concluded that the interaction with the pet, as such, is responsible, it is necessary to rule out other possible explanations. For instance, can the effect be attributed to dog owners taking more exercise? No significant differences emerged between dog owners and owners of other types of pet, in blood pressure, blood triacylglycerol or blood cholesterol levels. The researchers also looked into socio-economic status – perhaps the more affluent or better educated might be more likely to own pets? However, they found no difference in income or tertiary educational level between those with pets and those who did not have pets. These results might have important implications. They suggest that the reduction in systolic blood pressure attributable to pet ownership can be as large as that achieved by such interventions as salt and alcohol restriction. Even the modest reductions in cholesterol level observed here could dramatically lower the risk of cardiovascular disease.

5.3.4 Exercise

Introduction

During the course of the 20th century, there has been a dramatic rise in the percentage of us who lead a sedentary life, spending a large proportion of our time hunched over a desk at work and then slouched in front of the television in the evening eating high-energy snacks.

This section will present the evidence that even fairly mild physical exertion such as jogging or swimming for some minimal period, preferably each day, has advantages not just for the body (e.g. the cardiovascular system) but also for one's mental state. There is evidence that exercise can not only help to cure depression and anxiety but also help to prevent these states arising (Morgan and Goldston, 1987). Quite apart from anything as serious as depression, there is evidence that it can simply lift mood and help to give non-depressed people the much discussed 'feel-good factor'. The next section will look at the evidence for this.

Evidence for the role of exercise in promoting emotional health

The testimony of a very large number of participants in energetic sports such as jogging is that mood is elevated and a 'feel-good factor' is experienced (Morgan, 1981). It would seem that a minimum active period of about 20–30 minutes at least three times a week and preferably more frequently is needed to achieve the effect, which can last for up to 24 hours.

Unfortunately, many people drop out of exercise regimes before the beneficial effects have had time to appear; persistence is vital. Depression will often be reduced within 3–5 weeks. It is not simply anecdotal reports that lead to this conclusion. Psychological tests designed to reveal evidence of depression have shown a difference between sedentary and active subjects.

❑   Does that prove that activity causes the improved mental state?

■   On its own it doesn't prove this, since the causal link *might* be in the opposite direction; for example, individuals who are already depressed might shun activity. However, it is *consistent* with there being a causal link.

Stop and think for a while about how you would conduct an experiment to discover whether activity improves mood.

You would need to take subjects and divide them into two groups matched for sex, age, psychological state, etc. Measurements of their psychological state would be made at the outset. Then one group would engage in, say, jogging for a period of some weeks while the other group would engage in some inactive pursuit. They would then be compared for their psychological profiles. Such studies have been carried out and do indeed show an improvement in mood with activity for both non-depressed and depressed individuals (Johnsgard, 1989; Morgan and Goldston, 1987). The exercise groups showed decreases in hostility, anxiety and fatigue as well as increases in cheerfulness and reported 'energy'. To maintain these effects the person has to continue with the activity. A withdrawal effect, i.e. a move towards a depressed mood, can be shown when enforced inactivity follows a period of activity.

❑   Several times in this book already, you have come across the term 'placebo effect'. Is the concept of a placebo applicable to activity? Are there any particular difficulties raised here?

■   A possible placebo effect here would be if the changes in mood are the result not of physical exertion itself but of a belief in its efficacy. Also the presence of important-looking people with a vested interest in sport and with psychological profile scales ready to fill in might also be expected to influence subjects' responses.

The factor of control might have a significant positive placebo effect, e.g. the jogger's knowledge that a technique of self-medication is readily available. Unfortunately, one cannot take the equivalent of a placebo pill for exercise and so carry out a double-blind study. Most people probably know about the benefits of exercise and it is clear whether one has been allocated to the experimental or the control group! However, theoretically interesting as such issues are, they do not detract from the efficacy of exercise as a prescription for a healthier mental and physical life (Ransford, 1982).

Biological explanations of the effects of exercise on emotional health

Exercise involves a number of different physiological changes in the body, e.g. increased heart rate and blood flow, changes in secretion of hormones. There is also an increased blood flow to the central nervous system. It is difficult to tease apart the physiological changes and to find which are crucial to the psychological effects. Perhaps it is the combination of all of them that is important. The total physiological state accompanying a high level of physical activity might prove incompatible with unpleasant mental states, such as guilt. As Johnsgard argues:

> *Guilt is a passive sort of state, associated with deep sighs, shallow and infrequent breathing, a sluggish heartbeat, low blood pressure, and a listless, deenergized state. How can we feel guilt when our heart is pounding, our blood is surging, and our muscles and lungs are working near capacity?*

In addition to a possible influence of such general physiological changes, endorphins, released into the blood at times of physical exertion, are a strong candidate for a role in mood enhancement with exercise (Harte, Eifert and Smith, 1995). Meditation can also cause a rise in endorphin levels. As was discussed in Chapter 4, endorphins exert a pain-reducing effect. An examination of brain tissue in rats reveals that the occupation of opioid receptors increases following forced activity. In humans, the increase in endorphin secretion gets larger over weeks of daily exercise, mirroring the mood-enhancing effects that many people experience. It is believed that this might be implicated in the so-called 'runner's high', a euphoric state that some runners experience (Dishman, 1985). However, cognitive factors such as the expectation of a mood change and a feeling of mastery might be expected to act in complex interaction with any such endorphin influence in creating the 'high'. Endorphins are chemically similar to heroin and this might explain the withdrawal symptoms (e.g. anxiety, irritability, insomnia) that some regular exercisers experience with forced inactivity.

Research into depression has implicated abnormal levels of one or more of the following neurotransmitters in the central nervous system: dopamine, noradrenalin and serotonin. Which one of these plays the principal role has been a matter of some controversy, but it is safest to assume that they all play some role. The urine content of the metabolites (breakdown products) of these neurotransmitters is lower in depressed people (Ransford, 1982).

❑   What does this imply?

■   Less neurotransmitter is produced; therefore presumably its level of activity is lower.

So can exercise be considered the equivalent of taking antidepressants but without such undesirable side-effects as yawning, a dry mouth, dizziness and loss of orgasmic capacity? There is some evidence to support this view. Athletic rats have higher levels of serotonin and noradrenalin in their brain tissue following an enforced work-out (Johnsgard, 1989). Further evidence suggesting that exercise has similar effects to antidepressants in targeting certain neurotransmitters is the similarity in time course of the effect. From the start of regular exercise or antidepressant medication, it takes about 3–5 weeks for the effect to be felt. What is the biochemical basis of this delay? This is a fascinating question for which we don't yet have the answer. In the case of antidepressants that block neurotransmitter reuptake (Book 2, Chapter 3), their effect in elevating levels of neurotransmitter at the synapse appears to be much faster-acting than this. Thus we must be cautious not to assume a simple relationship between the amount of chemical at a synapse and mental health, since doubtless additional (e.g. cognitive) factors play a role. However, the evidence does suggest that the neurochemical state at certain synapses is one factor determining mental health and that changing it can help depressed people.

Summary of Section 5.3

1   The sense of belonging associated with membership of a religious or stable ethnic community with shared ideals seems to offer some protection against coronary heart disease.

2   Evidence suggests that the effect of social contact is mediated via the central nervous system exerting a restraint on the activation of the sympathetic nervous system.

3   An emotional, as well as a physical, health benefit is observed in people owning a pet.

4   Taking regular exercise is associated with decreases in hostility, anxiety and fatigue as well as increases in cheerfulness and a feeling of having energy.

5   Regular exercise can trigger the endorphin system. Beneficial effects on mood are probably also mediated via effects on neurotransmitter levels, e.g. serotonin.

5.4 Personality, behaviour and theories of stress and coronary function

We are often told to reduce our intake of fatty foods, smoke less, lose weight and take more exercise in order to achieve a healthier heart and circulation. Such appeals to change our habits are obviously important, but what is less well known in the UK is the role in coronary care of psychological factors related to personality. This section explores the relationship between (1) personality and behaviour and (2) the circulatory system. Coronary heart disease is still the number one killer in the USA (Williams, 1989), far outstripping cancer. At the time Williams was writing, the economic cost of heart disease in the USA was estimated at $100 billion per year, not to mention the social and emotional cost. So clearly, any intervention that could reduce this would be of immense importance. With large-scale epidemiological studies in the 1950s, the link between factors such as smoking, high blood pressure and high cholesterol levels, and the risk of suffering a heart attack was established. It was slightly later that the importance of the psychological factor of personality emerged.

Although links between psychological state and the condition of the heart have been recorded for some 4 500 years (first records derive from ancient Egypt) and appear in the Bible (Williams, 1989), scientific research on the role of personality in heart disease is most closely associated with two researchers from San Francisco, Meyer Friedman and Ray Rosenman. The message of their research is better known in the USA than in the UK. It is associated with the description of the so-called **Type A behaviour**, the person exhibiting such behaviour being termed a Type A. The Type A pattern is characterized by a person who is over-ambitious, in a hurry, aggressively competitive and easily aroused to anger and hostility by the kind of minor annoyances that plague much of our lives. By contrast, **Type B behaviour** is altogether more relaxed and lacking in competitiveness and hostility. The expressions 'Type A' and 'Type B' have entered the popular vocabulary, particularly in the USA. However, we should not see all people as necessarily fitting exactly one category or the other, though some do seem to exemplify the distinction. Rather, as with most personality characteristics, a person might be somewhere between the two or show features of each at various times.

The story began in the mid-1950s and the initial scientific insight came, not from a doctor or psychologist, but from a somewhat improbable source: an upholsterer. While inspecting the condition of the chairs in the San Francisco waiting room of cardiologists Drs Friedman and Rosenman, the upholsterer noted that the wear and tear was not even; whereas the front edge of the seats was badly worn the remainder was in a pristine condition. With the benefits of hindsight we would now suggest that the patients were predominantly the ever-alert Type As, who tended to sit on the edges of their seats. Fortunately, the upholsterer drew the attention of the receptionist to the observation, who in turn alerted Dr Friedman. Friedman did not attach much importance to the observation at the time but later reflected that it probably started a train of logic going that led to the Type A/Type B distinction.

So how does one determine who is a Type A? You might feel that this is simple, since doubtless by now you have identified a Type A or two known to you, if not actually yourself! But would Type As really give truthful answers, if they were aware of their personality traits? One cannot rely upon this, and so a more rigorous testing procedure is called for. Not only the content of the answer but the style of replying can be taken into account. As Williams (1989) so aptly expresses it:

> *Thus, if one responds to the question, 'Do you rush and hurry in doing most things?' before it is even finished, saying in a loud staccato voice, 'Hell no! I never allow outside demands to rule me!,' we would conclude that the content of the answer is Type B. The manner in which the answer is delivered, however, clearly portrays a very Type A outlook.*

The results clearly showed a relation between, on the one hand, the Type A personality and, on the other, both high blood cholesterol levels and a proneness to heart attacks.

Studies also showed correlations over the year between cholesterol levels and the occurrence of external events that tended to make subjects show strong Type A behaviour. For example, the blood cholesterol levels of a group of accountants were studied over a year and a pronounced increase was observed in the weeks that led up to 1 January and 15 April – the dates of tax deadlines.

By now you might be wondering whether the Type A personality as a factor in its own right contributes to increased incidence of heart disease, or whether the results might simply be explained by the fact that, say, Type As tend to smoke more than Type Bs or engage more in other high-risk behaviour. If this were the case, it would not diminish the interest of the data but would point to a different kind of explanation. However, careful statistical analysis showed that personality had an *independent* effect in its own right, contributing in interaction with other risk factors.

In spite of the undeniable value of the work on personality and coronary function, by the late 1970s and 1980s a number of studies had appeared that failed to show a clear relationship between Type A behaviour and coronary heart disease. Some follow-up studies failed to find an increased incidence of coronary disorder in Type As. A pioneer researcher in this area, Redford Williams attempted to explain this. While not doubting that there is some effect here, he argued that various aspects of a psychological make-up together constitute the Type A personality and not all of these are equally damaging. For instance, Williams argued that, taken on their own, the traits of being ambitious, competitive and feeling under time pressure are not damaging. The bad news is that hostility and anger constitute the components that are damaging to our circulatory system. According to Williams' analysis, being competitive and in a hurry are dangerous traits only in so far as they are likely to trigger anger and hostility. Otherwise they might even be beneficial for health. Williams argues:

> *If yours is a hostile heart, you need to change it into a more trusting heart.*

Williams' logic is as follows. With the excitement of the initial findings on personality, everyone had assumed a neat package of personality traits that are found together and which make up the Type A. These were a feeling of time pressure, a relentless striving for achievement and a relatively large amount of so-called 'free-floating' anger and hostility. Williams came to reason that maybe these traits did not necessarily always occur together. His writing, suggestive of a belief in a just Universe, might be of some inspiration to a struggling OU student:

> *Looking back, I know that I, like many others, found it hard to see why being ambitious should be so harmful; or even being in a hurry, for that matter. Hostility, on the other hand – well, it didn't take much imagination to see that aspect of Type A as something that, at the least, should be harmful.*

The role of hostility can be illustrated by considering the case of a real patient, John Smith (an assumed name), observed by Williams.

John Smith was a man who liked getting his own way and would let no one stop him. He was a successful businessman aged 44. Success relied upon him being able to bully his employees into submission. One afternoon, whilst driving in a hurry, John was overtaken by another car. John's usual reaction to such a situation would be to emit a blast on the horn and put his foot hard down to, in Williams' words, 'pay the bastard back'. However, this time John felt an awful sensation described as 'though a red-hot poker was being driven into the centre of his chest'. John had difficulty breathing, started to sweat profusely and felt very sick. This was his first heart attack. He was admitted to the coronary care unit of the local hospital.

The pain subsided. An ECG recording was made and its pattern found to be normal. John stayed in the hospital for several days and during that time experienced no symptoms. On his day of discharge, a technician made something of a mess of taking a blood sample; there were two unsuccessful attempts and then, just prior to a third, John decided enough was enough and rapidly geared up for a full-blown confrontation. Suddenly, as Williams expresses it, 'the red-hot poker hit his chest again'. An immediate ECG revealed that John's heart was not getting the blood supply that it needed. A later investigation revealed that one of the major coronary arteries was almost completely blocked by atherosclerotic plaque. A vein was subsequently transplanted from his leg to replace the blocked artery (i.e. John had a coronary bypass operation).

John was referred to Williams in the hope that Williams might be able to do something to help control the hostility. Williams' account of John's psychological make-up can serve to illustrate the traits that put a patient at risk. John never showed any trust in those under him in the business. Everyone was seen to be incompetent and needing to be checked and double-checked. John was prescribed a behaviour modification programme in order to try to get him to change his ways.

It was found subsequently by Williams that those patients with a high hostility score had particularly severe atherosclerotic blockage of the coronary arteries. The hostility score proved to be a more reliable predictor of arterial blockage than was a measure of the more general Type A behaviour.

❑　　Can you think of any possible explanation of this association, other than that psychological factors affect the circulation?

■　　It might be that hostile people smoke or drink more than others. It is also possible that coronary disorder might lead to hostility.

Careful statistical analysis of the results ruled out the first explanation.

❑　　How might you address the second possibility?

■　　One method is to measure hostility scores before the onset of coronary problems and see whether over the subsequent years this can be used to predict heart disorder.

Fortunately, data were available for a population in 1957 and could be used to see whether they could predict the frequency of coronary disorder in the 20 subsequent years. It was found that they could predict the incidence of not only coronary heart disease but also cancer. Figure 5.4 shows the strong relationship between potential for hostility and coronary arterial blockage, particularly for the younger section of the population.

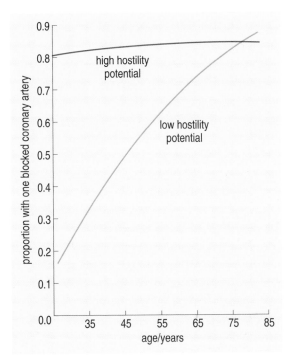

Figure 5.4　The proportion of subjects with one blocked coronary artery as a function of age. The two graphs are for subjects ranked either high or low in potential for hostility.

However, the story is not entirely a pessimistic one, even for those with a high hostility score. It is possible to change behaviour. Williams argues that learning doubtless plays a role in the development of the hostility profile. For example, to take a rather extreme case, an abused child is likely to grow up into an abuser. The experience of childhood abuse can be associated with difficulties in controlling aggression in a range of situations. Psychologists have emphasized the importance for normal development of the child being able to *trust* another individual. Some have associated in humans the basic mammalian pattern of nurturant care-giving with the development of altruism and social responsibility.

Comparisons between cultures are always fraught with difficulty and we need to be on guard against the common tendency to romanticize uncritically non-Western cultures. However, with suitable caution, some understanding can be gained. Williams believes that studying patterns of upbringing in different cultures can be insightful, and considers differences between America and Japan. Apparently, as discussed earlier in this chapter, Japanese children grow up in a culture which develops much closer social interaction and trusting interdependence than does American culture. Japanese mothers typically show closer physical proximity to their children and fewer signs of negative emotion. There is a greater emphasis upon the importance of developing good inter-personal skills. Researchers have found lower hostility scores for Japanese people than for Americans.

It is worth asking what keeps so many people healthy and living a rich life to a grand old age. Trust could be a factor. According to Williams, a trusting heart is one that is biased towards well-being; that is, the trusting heart:

> *…believes in the basic goodness of humankind, that most people will be fair and kind in relationships with others. Having such beliefs, the trusting heart is slow to anger.*

> *…the trusting heart spends little time feeling resentful, irritable and angry.*

Whereas hostility is a liability, trust can be of benefit to health. Williams advises the building of trust in children by rewarding with praise the performance of socially desirable behaviours such as showing cooperation and altruism. Treat children as if they are basically good, he urges. Of course, young children will model themselves on their parents' behaviour, so it is important that the parents show such altruism. So how do you acquire a more trusting heart? Trust is a complex thing. Clearly, at times it is right to be suspicious, since the consequences of a mistake can be horrendous. Where the danger of physical harm is present, as for example the prospect of a child going off with a stranger, it is obviously appropriate to be cautious. However, much of our mistrust of others concerns people we do not know and in all probability people who do *not* have bad motives. Furthermore, the issue over which our hostility is aroused is often one with trivial consequences. One trigger for hostility is the supermarket queue, exemplified by a thought such as: 'Why did that silly old goat have to choose this queue? He must have known I don't have time to spare'.

Williams has developed a programme for controlling such reactions, involving at first logging their occurrence and making a subsequent review.

If the patient finds him- or herself entertaining such thoughts then they are invited to counter them with a silent STOP command. Patients are then invited to challenge the logic underlying the negative thought. For example, in response to the negative 'supermarket' thought, try triggering yourself with a neutralizing thought of the kind: 'He is old. I will be old one day. He certainly doesn't have the intention of slowing me down', or 'Does it really matter if I am five minutes late. It is my heart that will suffer from my reaction, not his'. Within families, negative reactions and thoughts can be commonplace and can be written clearly on the face of the thinker. There is some evidence that they can be countered by neutralizing thoughts. This will not only be good for the heart of the negative thinker but will also make for greater family harmony.

Summary of Section 5.4

1   Personality and thereby style of reacting to the world plays an important role in coronary health and disease.

2   Some early investigations indicated a distinction between Type A and Type B personalities, with the former being more prone to coronary heart disease.

3   Subsequent work suggests that one particular trait associated more with the Type A personality, that of excessive hostility, is the crucial factor.

4   Various techniques can be employed in an effort to lower the hostility reaction.

5   Excessive sympathetic nervous system reactivity in hostility appears to be the biological basis of these effects.

5.5 The immune system, behaviour and health

The links from the nervous system to the immune system are both direct and mediated via hormones (Figure 5.5). There is also a reciprocal link: the nervous system is influenced by events in the immune system. The growing recognition of the link from the nervous system (and thereby emotion) to the immune system has been embraced by certain popular and uncritical writers – the fact that effects of mental states on immune function can be shown to occur has, in the hands of some, led to the argument that virtually all bodily dysfunctions can be explained in psychological terms; for example, the reader is encouraged to believe cancer is simply the product of a disturbed mind. From the scientific evidence, although the nervous system has been shown to affect the functioning of the immune system, a much more critical approach is indicated, in which a multitude of factors are implicated in often complex and contradictory ways.

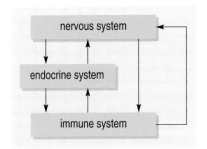

Figure 5.5   The interdependence of the nervous, endocrine and immune systems.

There is a large number of experimental reports indicating that, in a wide variety of different situations and with various species, humans included, stress can inhibit the activity of the immune system. However, the effects can be subtle and occasionally stressors even boost the immune system or have no apparent effect. There is an attractive simplicity in attributing most things to a single psychological construct like stress. However, in reality, this psychological effect is most likely only one (albeit important) factor amongst very many that influence the immune system and susceptibility to disease.

It is worth cautioning against the idea that there is a single and simple state that can be termed 'stress'. Rather, there is the possibility that different stressors might activate differently the corticosteroid and adrenalin/noradrenalin control systems, with possibly complex effects upon the immune system. Also, a stressor might depress one function of the immune system, but have no effect on another. Bearing these cautions in mind, it has been noted that such acute stressors as student examinations (sorry about that one!), a period of vigilance in combat and sleep deprivation, as well as more chronic stressful conditions such as divorce, depression, bereavement and caring for someone with Alzheimer's disease, all lower immune response in humans (Maier, Watkins and Fleshner, 1994). For practical as well as ethical reasons, it is very difficult to do relevant experiments on humans. However, in studies using rats it has been found that the activity of immune system cells is decreased when the animal is exposed to controlled stressors.

Thus we need to be cautious about blanket claims of the kind 'stress depresses immune function' and make the more qualified assertion that 'certain stressors under certain conditions can affect some parts of the immune system'. Also stressors might have an impact on disease through routes other than the immune system (Maier et al., 1994). Stressors change a variety of physiological parameters, e.g. blood flow to the various parts of the body. Furthermore, stressors such as divorce or bereavement change a host of different behaviours such as sleep, exercise, and food, alcohol and cigarette consumption, any of which might crucially impinge upon disease susceptibility.

What is the evidence that the nervous system can affect the immune system? First, we will consider the direct link. As was noted in Book 2, Chapter 5, there are neurons of the ANS that innervate the organs of the immune system, e.g. thymus, bone marrow, spleen and lymph nodes (Maier et al., 1994). Neurons of the sympathetic branch of the ANS that innervate these organs release the transmitter noradrenalin. There are receptors for noradrenalin at both the organs of the immune system and on the mobile cells of the system. Another link is mediated by corticosteroids. As described earlier in this chapter, these hormones are released into the bloodstream in response to stressors, amongst other things. Some cells of the immune system have receptors for corticosteroids on their surface. Occupation of these receptors by corticosteroids tends to inhibit the cell's activity.

Thus there is clearly the potential for the nervous system to affect the immune system. The evidence from electrical stimulation and lesioning of the brains of non-human animals is that activity in the CNS, especially the hypothalamus, does indeed affect the immune system. There is also evidence from the ubiquitous phenomenon of conditioning. You have met conditioning already (e.g. in Book 3, Chapter 6, in the context of Pavlov's salivary conditioning experiment) and it has also been discussed in earlier parts of the present book. If a drug is injected that suppresses the immune system, then cues paired with the drug will tend on their own to acquire some of the capacity of the drug with which they were paired, a **conditioned immunosuppressive effect**. This effect is best explained by postulating nervous system processes to be underlying the conditioning. The cues associated with the drug (e.g. sight of needle, feel of injection) are detected by sensory neurons and the information is transmitted to the CNS.

Such conditioning can be of some practical importance in a hospital context (Maier *et al.*, 1994). Chemotherapeutic drugs given to treat cancer act by inhibiting the division of rapidly replicating cells, including cancer cells. Unfortunately, they tend also to inhibit the replication of some perfectly benign cells including those of the immune system. If the chemotherapy is given repeatedly in the same setting, there is the possibility that cues within the environment will come to exert a conditioned immunosuppressive effect. Indeed, in one study, it was found that women who had received a series of chemotherapeutic treatments for ovarian cancer showed a response of immunosuppression merely on entering the hospital prior to the chemotherapy.

❑   How might one try to prevent such a conditioned effect arising?

◼   One possibility is to try to make changes in the context in which the therapy is given, though this might prove difficult.

Summary of Section 5.5

1   The nervous system (and thereby emotion) is able to influence the immune system both directly and via hormones.

2   There is evidence that, under some conditions, stress can inhibit the activity of the immune system.

3   Some of the effects on the immune system are mediated by corticosteroids, which can depress immune function.

4   An environment associated with depression of the immune system can become a conditional stimulus.

5.6 Conclusions

A theme that emerges from the chapter is that we can sometimes take actions that have effects upon the processes that underlie our emotions and associated physiological reactions. Confronted with stressors, we often have some degrees of freedom. The health benefits of positive social interaction in the sense of community spirit and belonging seem to be beyond doubt. Researchers believe that hostility is harmful to health.

You may be certain that the neural–hormonal systems that underlie the reaction to a stressor can serve a useful biological function when activated *under appropriate conditions*. So much then depends upon knowing what these appropriate conditions are. It is presumably not difficult to accept that, if you were confronted with a charging bull, an accelerated heart rate and a high rate of secretion of corticosteroids could be to your advantage. You might also accept that such activation is generally not to your advantage when waiting in a long queue at the supermarket check-out. However, these days, at least in urban Britain, the situations in which stress hormone activation occurs are more likely to be characterized by the the supermarket queue rather than the charging bull. Therefore, there would seem to be the scope for stress management, either through formal programmes or simply by homespun personal monitoring schemes. Concerning the links between the nervous system and the immune system, as you saw in Book 2, Chapter 5, it is possible to argue logically that, at times, inhibition of both an immune response and inflammation is advantageous. In practice, however, it would seem that some of the inhibition could be maladaptive when considered in the context of a chronically stressful lifestyle.

As far as development is concerned, for emotional health the message is one of providing a warm nurturing environment to children, with role models of trusting bonds, altruism and cooperation and the avoidance of undue hostility. Complete sheltering from all possible stressors is not recommended. Some short-term activation of the stress-hormone systems is not dangerous provided it is in an appropriate context and actions are available to correct the impact of the stressors. For example, it might be worth incurring a few kicks on the football pitch in order to derive the benefits of exercise and to develop a more resilient emotional and stress-hormone system for later years.

Objectives for Chapter 5

After completing this chapter you should be able to:

5.1 Define and use, or recognize definitions and applications of, each of the terms printed in **bold** in the text.

5.2 Give an account of why the study of emotional health and stress requires an holistic approach that takes into account personality and the interactions between the nervous, endocrine and immune systems. (*Question 5.1*)

5.3   Outline some of the main physiological changes that occur at times of emotion. (*Questions 5.2 and 5.3*)

5.4   Offer some practical advice for achieving a lowering of negative emotions and an increase in the weight of positive emotions, as well as a rationale for its efficacy. (*Question 5.4*)

5.5   Explain some of the means by which events in the nervous system can influence those in the immune system. (*Question 5.5*)

Questions for Chapter 5

Question 5.1   (*Objective 5.1*)

Suppose you were to be confronted by a no-nonsense sceptic, who ridicules the message of part of this chapter. The sceptic laughs at the idea that belonging to a church or keeping a pet dog can influence your health. 'Health is matter of the physical body', the sceptic argues, 'You are going soft in the head with all this superstitious and mystical nonsense'. What might you say to the sceptic in response (assuming you do not agree, that is!)?

Question 5.2   (*Objective 5.3*)

In the text you met the expression 'hypothalamic pituitary adrenocortical system'. Explain what is meant by this term in such a way that shows the links between the nervous and endocrine systems.

Question 5.3   (*Objective 5.3*)

In what way might CRH be described as an atypical hormone?

Question 5.4   (*Objective 5.4*)

What might constitute biological evidence that a behavioural therapy programme involving thought-changing is effective?

Question 5.5   (*Objective 5.5*)

Given the availability of rat subjects, how might you test for the ability of the immune system to show conditioned immunosuppression? Explain the procedure and any result in terms of classical (Pavlovian) conditioning (Book 3, Chapter 6, and Chapter 4 of this book).

References

Anderson, W. P., Reid, C. M. and Jennings, G. L. (1992) Pet ownership and risk factors for cardiovascular disease, *The Medical Journal of Australia*, **157**, 298–301.

Bovard, E. W. (1985) Brain mechanisms in effects of social support on viability, in *Perspectives in Behavioural Medicine*, **2**, R. B. Williams (ed), Orlando, pp. 103–129.

Dishman, R. K. (1985) Medical psychology in exercise and sport, *Medical Clinics of North America*, **69**, 123–143.

Friedlander, Y., Kark, J. D. and Stein, Y. (1986) Religious orthodoxy and myocardial infarction in Jerusalem – a case control study, *International Journal of Cardiology*, **10**, 33–41.

Friedlander, Y., Kark, J. D. and Stein, Y. (1987) Religious observance and plasma lipids and lipoproteins among 17-year-old Jewish residents of Jersusalem, *Preventive Medicine*, **16**, 70–79.

Harte, J. L., Eifert, G. H. and Smith, R. (1995) The effects of running and meditation on beta-endorphin, corticotropin-releasing hormone and cortisol in plasma, and on mood, *Biological Psychology*, **40**, 251–265.

House, J. S., Landis, K. R. and Umberson, D. (1988) Social relationships and health, *Science*, **241**, 540–545.

Johnsgard, K. W. (1989) *The Exercise Prescription for Depression and Anxiety*, Plenum Press, New York.

Maier, S. F., Watkins, L. R. and Fleshner, M. (1994) Psychoneuroendocrinology, *American Psychologist*, **49**, 1004–1017.

Marmot, M. G. and Syme, S. L. (1976) Acculturation and coronary heart disease in Japanese-Americans, *American Journal of Epidemiology*, **104**, 225–247.

Morgan, W. P. (1981) Psychological benefits of physical activity, in *Exercise in Health and Disease*, F. J. Nagle and H. J. Montoye (eds), C. C. Thomas, Springfield, pp. 299–314.

Morgan, W. P. and Goldston, S. E. (1987) *Exercise and Mental Health*, Hemisphere Publishing Corporation, Washington.

Oxman, T. E., Freeman, D. H. and Manheimer, E. D. (1995) Lack of social participation or religious strength and comfort as risk factors for death after cardiac surgery in the elderly, *Psychosomatic Medicine*, **57**, 5–15.

Ransford, C. P. (1982) A role for amines in the antidepressant effect of exercise: a review, *Medicine and Science in Sports and Exercise*, **14**, 1–10.

Siegel, J. M. (1990) Stressful life events and use of physician services among the elderly: the moderating role of pet ownership, *Journal of Personality and Social Psychology*, **58**, 1081–1086.

Serpell, J. (1991) Beneficial effects of pet ownership on some aspects of human health and behaviour, *Journal of the Royal Society of Medicine*, **84**, pp. 717–720.

Toates, F. (1995) *Stress – Conceptual and Biological Aspects*, Wiley, Chichester.

Williams, R. (1989) *The Trusting Heart*, Times Books, New York.

Williams, R. B. (1995) A relook at personality types and coronary heart disease. *Progress in Cardiology*, **4**, 91–97.

CHAPTER 6
SLEEP

6.1 Introduction

Sleep occupies a considerable portion of most of our lives and yet no one really knows exactly why we need to sleep. Thus, a large part of the discussion in Chapter 6 will, of necessity, be somewhat speculative. Some possible hypotheses to account for sleep will be explored. This lack of a secure knowledge base is fundamental to how the investigation of sleep is approached. By contrast, there is little doubt as to the biological function of, say, feeding, drinking and sex, and therefore the way that they are able to be discussed is rather different from sleep.

Sleep can be defined as a state of 'unconsciousness from which the person can be aroused by sensory or other stimuli' (Guyton, 1991, p. 659). In such terms, sleep stands in distinction from a **coma**, which is a state of unconsciousness from which the person cannot be woken. Sleep is not a single unitary state but something which varies in quality and depth. At times during a night's sleep the eyes can be observed to be showing rapid movements, in the form of small angular rotations in their sockets, termed **rapid eye movements**. Using this index, researchers commonly divide sleep into two different types or phases, known as **rapid-eye-movement sleep** (REM sleep) and **non-rapid-eye-movement sleep** (NREM sleep). In turn, using other criteria, NREM sleep can be divided into various phases (see Figure 6.1, for example).

The classification of sleep is based upon a number of criteria such as the electrical activity of the brain, the presence or absence of rapid eye movements and the reports of the sleeping experience of the individual on being woken at a particular stage of sleep. REM sleep is characterized by a level of metabolism of the brain comparable to the waking state, whereas NREM sleep is associated with an overall decrease in brain metabolism.

Most of us go through one complete cycle of getting up, working, going to bed, sleeping and waking up every 24 hours, which is then repeated. The 24 hours is termed the *period* of the cycle. The evidence is that sleep forms part of what is termed a **circadian rhythm**. This expression refers to a rhythm that meets two criteria. First, it takes approximately 24 hours to complete one cycle and, second, it is internally generated, i.e. arising within the processes of the body itself.

❑   In itself, the fact that sleep and waking show a rhythm with a period of 24 hours does not prove that sleep is part of a circadian rhythm. Why not?

■   The rhythm might not be internally driven. The 24-hour cycle of light and dark in the world as well as social factors such as work and even breakfast television might serve to determine the rhythm.

Clearly, such factors do play a role in setting the precise timing of the rhythm. When you move to another country you adjust to the new social factors and changed timing of light/dark. These factors are given the term **zeitgeber** from the German expressions *zeit* (time) and *geber* (giver). However, the scientific evidence strongly suggests that there is also an intrinsically generated rhythm that underlies our cycle of activity and inactivity.

❏   Can you speculate as to how investigators might discover whether such a rhythm exists?

■   Subjects can be put in a special environment in which, as far as is possible, zeitgebers have been eliminated.

In practice, this means locating subjects somewhere like in a deep mine under conditions of constant illumination. When this has been done, the gallant volunteers continue to show a rhythm having a period of approximately 24 hours. This strongly points to the existence of a circadian rhythm.

The following section looks more closely at two different phases of sleep. After this the brain processes underlying sleep are discussed. The chapter then turns to theories on the function served by sleep and finally looks at some practical applications of an understanding of sleep. The chapter draws heavily on work by Horne (1988); if you are particularly interested in sleep his book is well worth reading.

Summary of Section 6.1

1   Sleep can be divided into two types, rapid-eye-movement sleep (REM sleep) and non-rapid-eye-movement sleep (NREM sleep).

2   A circadian rhythm is an intrinsically produced rhythm that has a period of about 24 hours. Sleep is programmed to occur as part of a circadian rhythm.

6.2 Types of sleep

6.2.1 Introduction

The body organ that shows the clearest change between sleep and relaxed wakefulness is the brain. It is possible to observe the brain's electrical activity by making recordings from its surface or (as is easier and more usual) from the surface of the head, with attached electrodes. In this way, the overall electrical activity of regions of the brain – particularly its outer layer, the cerebral cortex (Book 2, Chapter 3) – is observed. This record is made up from the combined activity of millions of individual neurons.

Such a study is termed **electroencephalography** (EEG for short); an alternative name for the cerebral cortex is 'encephalon' and so the study refers to the recording of the activity of this region. The record is termed an *electroencephalogram* (also abbreviated as EEG). Because it looks only at the activity in the superficial brain regions, the EEG tells us nothing about what is happening electrically in deeper regions of the brain. Implanted electrodes could tell us this but of course usually it is not ethically possible to perform such studies on humans.

The EEG shows characteristic changes between states of sleep and waking – see Figure 6.1 for example. One phase of NREM sleep which we shall consider is termed **slow-wave sleep** (SWS).

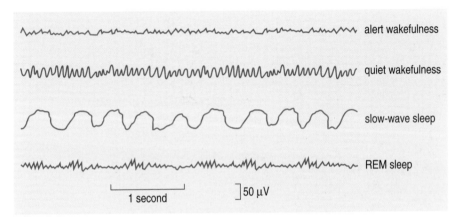

Figure 6.1   Electrical activity at different phases of sleep.

The significance of the EEG is that the voltage changes generated by individual neurons are too small to be detected at such a distance between neuron and electrode. The fact that coherent patterns of voltage change can be recorded with the EEG implies that many neurons are synchronized in their activity and thereby their effects are added together.

6.2.2 Slow-wave sleep

Most of the night's sleep is of the slow-wave variety, so called because an EEG reveals the presence of slow waves of electrical activity, shown in Figure 6.1. This phase of sleep is therefore sometimes termed *synchronized sleep*, meaning that the activity of many neurons is synchronized so as to give a relatively large signal.

Slow-wave sleep (SWS) is characterized as a particularly restful phase of sleep with associated decrease in blood pressure, basal metabolic rate and respiratory rate. SWS is also termed 'dreamless sleep' but this is something of a misnomer since dreams do sometimes occur during this phase. However, the dreams that occur in SWS tend not to be remembered, unlike those in REM sleep.

6.2.3 REM sleep

In distinction to slow-wave sleep, the relatively low amplitude of rhythms in the REM phase (see Figure 6.1) gives this the alternative title *desynchronized sleep*, though of course considerable synchrony must still occur for even the low-amplitude rhythms to appear. In human adults, bouts of REM sleep are observed during the night every 90 minutes or so. The bouts last about 5–30 minutes. When the EEG reveals this pattern, rapid eye movements are observed. The first appearance of REM sleep is usually at 80–100 minutes following the onset of sleep. REM sleep is also termed *paradoxical sleep*, the paradox being that the brain shows electrical activity characteristic of waking and yet the person is deep in sleep (see Figure 6.1). In REM sleep the brain is very active and brain metabolism is relatively high.

REM sleep is particularly associated with dreaming. People who are woken during this phase commonly report dreaming. The threshold for waking someone is higher (i.e. they are more difficult to wake) during REM sleep than SWS. Heart rate and respiration rate show irregular patterns of activity. An inhibition is exerted on the activation of most muscles throughout the body. However, the muscles that control the activity of the eyes in their sockets function normally in REM sleep, as indicated by the eye movements that characterize this phase. Some have speculated that the eye movements correspond to the eyes scanning the contents of the dream.

Summary of Section 6.2

1   Electroencephalography (EEG) is a technique for examining the electrical activity of the outer region of the brain.

2   Slow-wave sleep is characterized by synchronization of the activity of relatively many neurons, as shown by EEG recording.

3   The REM phase of sleep is associated with desynchronized activity. It is sometimes termed paradoxical sleep.

6.3 The biological bases of sleep

6.3.1 Neural mechanisms

The biological basis of sleep, as with any other behavioural phenomenon, consists of different brain regions acting in complex interaction. Giving particular responsibility to certain brain regions should only be done in the context of considering these interactions. With these cautions in mind, in the case of sleep, a particular role can be attributed to certain brain regions. For example, we can ask questions of the following kind. Are there brain regions that are particularly responsible for generating the circadian rhythm that underlies sleep? Are there regions whose functioning in terms of, say, metabolism or processing information is particularly affected by sleep and by sleep loss? Are there hormones or neurotransmitters that target certain brain regions or have a high concentration there and have an especially important role in sleep?

❑   Based upon what you learned in Book 2, Chapter 3, try to think of the kind of evidence that could be used to answer these questions.

■   The evidence might come from patients who have suffered damage to regions of the brain and who subsequently show abnormal sleep patterns. In some cases, human brains might have been electrically stimulated during the course of surgical interventions and effects on sleep noted. Animal brains might have been lesioned or stimulated electrically and changes in sleep patterns measured. The effects on sleep of agonists and antagonists for particular neurotransmitters could be investigated.

We know that sleep is not simply a passive state that arises when, say, a population of neurons fatigues. Rather it is an active state produced by patterns of neural activity. Sleep can be induced by stimulating certain brain regions.

One brain region that has a role in sleep is the reticular formation, introduced in Book 2, Chapter 3 (see Figure 6.2). Animal studies have shown that lesions made in the reticular formation have a particularly disruptive effect upon the pattern of sleep–waking. Evidence suggests that neurons employing the neurotransmitter acetylcholine are involved in the neural processes in the reticular formation that underlie sleep.

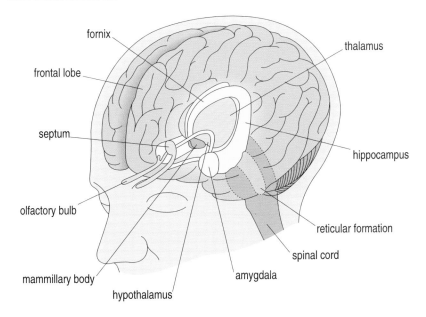

Figure 6.2   The location of the reticular formation.

Figure 6.3 shows the role of the reticular formation. Sensory information is conveyed to specific parts of the brain in what is sometimes termed the *classical sensory pathways*, for example touch and noxious information. However, collaterals (branches) of these axons project to the reticular formation. Sensory stimulation will thereby stimulate the reticular formation. In turn, the reticular formation projects axons to the cerebral cortex. By means of these projections, the cortex can be put in an alert as opposed to a sleepy state.

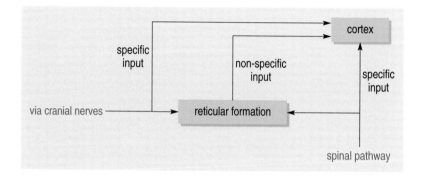

Figure 6.3   The role of the reticular formation. The specific pathways carry detailed sensory information directly to the cortex. Note the collaterals to the reticular formation. In turn the reticular formation sends non-specific information to the cerebral cortex, i.e. it sensitizes the cortex.

The stimulation of several areas near the base of the brain can induce sleep (Guyton, 1991). Injection of agents that prevent the synthesis of serotonin prevent sleep, which implies that serotonergic neurons (i.e. those that secrete the neurotransmitter serotonin) play a major role in the organization of sleep. Another neurotransmitter that appears to be implicated is dopamine. Part of the evidence here concerns the actions in humans of substances that boost the levels of dopamine at synapses. Such substances, which include cocaine and amphetamines, have the effect of increasing wakefulness. Conversely, when the drugs become unavailable, long-term users can experience a state of withdrawal from them, associated with an increase in sleep.

Perhaps the most obvious thing about sleep is its cyclical nature. As noted earlier, this is found even when people have been placed in sensory isolation from the familiar cues of light–dark and the social events that occur throughout the cycle. For example, one subject spent time in isolation deep in a cave in France. He still showed a clear rhythm, though its period was slightly longer than the usual 24 hours. There appears to be an intrinsic rhythm-generator within the central nervous system that programmes the cycle of sleep and waking. However, although this rhythm is generated internally, it will *entrain on* (meaning 'lock on to') the light–dark cycles and social activities of the outside world.

So which brain regions play a role in the cyclical aspect of sleep? The evidence suggests that a particular region termed the *suprachiasmatic nucleus* (SCN) (Figure 6.4) is involved both in generating the rhythm and in relating the light–dark cycles of the external world to the intrinsic rhythm of sleep in such a way that the latter tends to shift into phase with the former. Pathways leading from the retina inform the SCN on the state of light–dark of the external world (the optic nerve is one of the cranial nerves shown in Figure 6.3). In animal studies, it has been found that lesioning of·the SCN has a profound effect upon the timing of sleep, the circadian rhythm being disrupted.

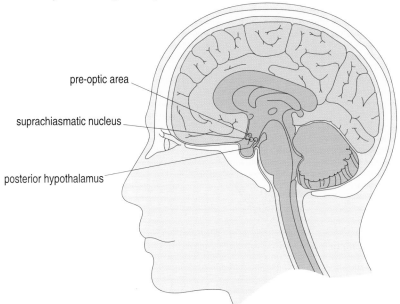

Figure 6.4   The brain showing the suprachiasmatic nucleus.

How does a collection of neurons generate a rhythmic signal that serves as a clock? We don't know. There is evidence that in rats the neurons in the SCN show a powerful rhythm in their metabolic activity. Recordings have been made of the electrical activity (the frequency of action potentials) of single neurons in the SCN. Such activity exhibits a circadian rhythm.

Body temperature also shows a circadian rhythm, it normally being lower during sleep than during the period of waking, as shown in Figure 6.5. This rhythm is independently generated within the central nervous system and does not simply depend upon the rhythm of sleep.

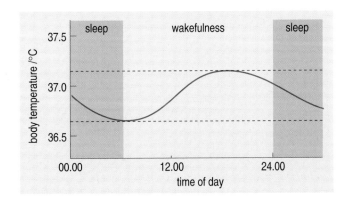

Figure 6.5   Rhythms of sleep and body temperature.

6.3.2 A sleep factor?

Is there such a thing as a *sleep factor* (i.e. a natural chemical) present in the blood that will induce sleep if injected into an animal? Some researchers have managed to extract a substance from the fluid in the ventricles (see Book 2, Chapter 3) within the brain of sleep-deprived goats. When injected into other animals, this so-called 'Factor S' was quickly followed by sleep. Some investigators have been able to identify Factor S in human urine and to extract it. Three thousand litres of urine were required to obtain just seven-millionths of a gram of Factor S. Injected into rabbits, it caused large increases in sleep.

Study of the mechanisms underlying any behaviour can be illuminated by considerations of the function that behaviour serves. Since we understand rather little about the mechanisms underlying sleep and the function that they serve, speculation tends to build upon speculation. The following section looks at the function of sleep and attempts to relate it to the biological bases of sleep as discussed in the present section.

Summary of Section 6.3

1   Dividing up the brain into regions and allocating responsibility for special functions to particular areas is fraught with difficulty. However, the evidence suggests that certain regions do have an especially important role in sleep, one being the reticular formation.

2   Evidence derived from artificially boosting dopamine levels by administering drugs indicates that dopamine plays a role in increasing wakefulness.

3   Although sleep is programmed by an intrinsic circadian rhythm, it can be influenced by outside factors, the suprachiasmatic nucleus having a special role in mediating this influence.

4   Research is directed to identifying a sleep factor.

6.4 The function of sleep

6.4.1 Introduction

The function that sleep serves is still something of a mystery and there are a number of theories. To give a complete explanation of the function of sleep, a combination of all of the theories might well be necessary. These theories fall roughly into three categories, as follows:

1   Sleep is needed for a *restorative function* following 'the "wear and tear" of wakefulness' (discussed by Horne, 1988, p. 25). One version of this theory suggests that, during waking hours, some chemical builds up or gets depleted in the body (for example, neurotransmitter levels might be reduced in certain brain regions, or fatigue of regions of the central nervous system occurs). A proposal that sleep serves to 'restore the

natural balance among the neural centres' (Guyton, 1991, p. 661) is similar to this.

2   Sleep serves the function of *keeping us out of harm's way* when we are at our most vulnerable (Meddis, 1977). Thus, the human species, with rather poor night vision, stays asleep and therefore inactive and sheltered at night. Nocturnal animals such as rats, which make more use of other senses such as touch and smell, are active at a time when their predators have more difficulty catching them.

3   Sleep serves to *'re-program' the brain*. It is necessary for a kind of library cataloguing process to occur such that new experiences can be assimilated into memory. Some writers assume that such re-programming serves to solve inner emotional conflicts.

This section will draw on various bits of evidence to bear on the issue of the function of sleep, starting with a closer look at the three explanations just outlined.

6.4.2   Evidence relating to the theories of sleep

A restorative function?

Sleep does not appear to be necessary for maintaining the function of the body outside the nervous system. For instance, there is no evidence to suggest that correction of muscular fatigue is the function served by sleep. The functioning of organs outside of the nervous system is not impaired by sleep loss *as far as is known*. However, it is known that the functioning of the central nervous system (its processing of information) is impaired by lack of sleep. A person can be made neurotic as a result of sleep deprivation.

If explanation (1) above were true then we might rather easily be able to link the cause and function of sleep. In other words, if sleep has evolved to serve some such restorative role, it might be that a state of disequilibrium serves to motivate sleep, and restoration of equilibrium would move us to waking.

❏   Of what process already described would this be a case?

■   Homeostasis.

Keeping us out of harm's way?

Suppose explanation (2) is correct and sleep evolved as a process to keep us inactive at times of vulnerability. What would provide the signal for sleep? We know that there is a circadian rhythm underlying sleep. Thus we know that the system would still involve some kind of physiological mechanism in the form of an oscillation motivating sleep at appropriate times within the circadian rhythm. The difference from explanation (1) is not in terms of the presence or absence of an internal signal, since either explanation involves this. Rather, whereas explanation (1) suggests that sleep evolved to serve the function of maintaining the internal physiological variable within limits, explanation (2) suggests that changes in the physiological variable evolved simply as a way of programming sleep.

In principle, according to explanation (2), if sleep is not serving a restorative function, it might be possible to overcome sleep. For instance, a substance might be discovered that is an antagonistic to neurotransmitters underlying sleep. People might then take such a substance to overcome sleep. Given the help of artificial lighting to stop us falling into rivers or off mountains, we might then experience no harmful effects of being active throughout 24 hours. The benefits for such things as TMA completion by the cut-off date hardly need mentioning.

Re-programming the brain?

On the basis of explanation (3) – that sleep serves to re-program the brain – it might seem surprising that you often feel equally sleepy after a busy day with work and SK220 as after a day of lounging in the sun doing nothing. However, even if (3) could explain why sleep evolved, again there might need to be an intrinsic oscillatory signal to account for the timing of sleep. Underlying explanation (3) is the idea that sleep might be necessary to allow memory consolidation to occur. New experiences encountered throughout the day might be better assimilated into memory during sleep. However, this is an area of some controversy.

A combination of all three?

A combination of the three explanations might ultimately prove to be the most accurate. Thus, in terms of explanation (2), we are inactive at times when, in our evolutionary history, there has been little to be gained and much to be lost by activity. Bodily resources can be conserved. It is known that during sleep the sympathetic nervous system (Book 2, Chapter 3) is relatively inactive and the parasympathetic dominant. This causes a reduction in arterial pressure, heart rate and metabolic rate. Muscles are relaxed. In terms of explanation (1), some disturbance in the central nervous system (e.g. excess levels of neurotransmitter or a product of metabolism) would motivate sleep, which corrects the disturbance. If this disturbance is not corrected the function of the brain is impaired in some way. During this time the brain can be re-programmed (explanation 3).

Horne (1988) suggests that sleep serves two main functions. First, it serves to perform some kind of neuronal repair function within the brain, though we lack hard evidence for this. For instance, synapses might need to be restructured or enzymes crucial for processes within the neuron might need to be restored to optimal levels. Horne suggested that this repair normally occurs in the first few hours of sleep. The amount of sleep needed to allow such repair is termed **core sleep** by Horne. It corresponds to periods of both SWS and REM sleep. The remainder of the body does not require sleep for repair; relaxed wakefulness suffices. However, Horne suggests that neuronal repair might not explain the length of normal sleep, since repair could take less time to perform than that which we normally spend sleeping. If this is the case, then the remainder of sleep might serve simply to keep us inactive at a time when it is disadvantageous to be active (e.g. risk of accidents, use of energy to little gain). Horne terms such sleep **optional sleep**. Optional sleep is programmed by a motivational process that is heavily dependent upon a circadian rhythm. Thus the chief pressure for optional sleep is the time within the circadian rhythm. At a certain point in the circadian cycle we are simply programmed to feel sleepy. By contrast, in so far as core sleep is concerned, the pressure to sleep comes not from the time of day but from the length of time that has elapsed since the last sleep.

Thus, based upon the considerations discussed in this section, some researchers propose a two-factor theory of sleep, as shown in Figure 6.6 (Horne, 1988; de Jesus Cabeza, Zoltoski and Gillin, 1994). Figure 6.6a shows the circadian influence on sleep. Figure 6.6b shows a tendency to sleep that increases as a function of the length of time since the last sleep. This would represent some kind of disturbance to homeostasis, though exactly what we do not know. The strength of tendency to sleep might be expected to be dependent upon both factors, as represented in Figure 6.6c.

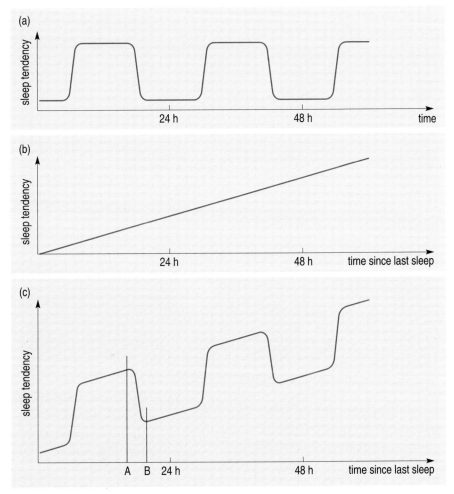

Figure 6.6 The tendency to sleep (a) arising from the circadian rhythm, (b) arising from some kind of neuronal repair process, and (c) the combination of the two factors.

Normally, neuronal repair would occur at the early stages of the sleep period, programmed largely by the cycle of optional sleep. If, however, a night or two's sleep is missed, in spite of the motivation to continue with wakefulness, the dictates of the core sleep system might switch in and mean that sleep occurs.

Lesions to the suprachiasmatic nucleus (SCN), discussed in Section 6.3.1, appear to leave the contribution to sleep represented in Figure 6.6b unaffected. That is to say, the tendency to sleep arises as a function of the time since the last sleep. The other sleep factor (Figure 6.6a), i.e. the circadian factor motivating us to sleep at certain points within the 24-hour cycle, is disrupted by lesions to the SCN.

With reference to Figure 6.6c, note that a person might feel *less* sleepy at time B than at time A (for example), even though they have been deprived of sleep for more time.

Having shown a graph of the kind in Figure 6.6a, it is necessary to point out a possible complication with it. The graph rightly indicates a peak at the night phase but in practice there is also a small peak in sleep tendency in the mid-afternoon, appropriately coinciding with the siesta time observed in some cultures. For whatever reason, mid-afternoon can be a problematic time for academics trying to keep audiences awake and for drivers at the wheel.

6.4.3 Comparative studies

It is often possible to gain some insight into human behaviour by studying other species and making cautious comparisons. In the case of sleep, since it is something of an enigma as to why we sleep, it might be that particular insights could be gained by looking at how sleep is organized in other species and then drawing comparisons.

One of the first striking things about sleep is that it is observed in most species so far investigated, including all mammals. A number of different mammalian species have been studied ranging widely in lifestyle and yet all exhibit sleep to some extent. This ubiquitous presence might suggest that sleep serves some vital biological function quite apart from being an efficient way of passing some time when there is little better to do.

Dolphins are particularly interesting subjects to study. They have a well-developed brain, and Horne (1988) suggests that restitution of the brain is the explanation of why they sleep. The natural habitat in which some dolphins live is such that sleep appears to put their immediate safety at risk yet they still show bouts of sleep. This suggests that such sleep is necessary to serve a vital restorative role. The relatively brief periods of sleep would constitute core sleep. For example, the Indus dolphin is blind and relies upon its highly effective sonar system. It lives in muddy waters subject to considerable turbulence. In the monsoon season, the waters contain a variety of debris, such as uprooted trees. Life requires eternal vigilance for the Indus dolphin; alertness is imperative as it needs to avoid obstacles being carried by the water and prevent itself from being swept against rocks at the bed of the river. A cessation of active swimming for long would of course be hazardous. Incredibly, the dolphin seems to get a considerable amount of sleep, taken in the form of naps of only a few seconds' duration many times a day.

Researchers in Moscow have made a study of two species of dolphin, the bottlenose dolphin and porpoise, which are found in the Black Sea. By the use of electrodes, they were able to study the electrical activity of these species' brains. Sleep took on a bizarre form in which each half-brain took it in turns to sleep. This meant that some kind of vigilance could be maintained at all times, even if with only a half-brain for some of the time. Total sleep was some 12 hours, made up of 2-hour shifts of sleep between the half-brains. This suggests that some restitution role is being carried out in the sleeping half-brain.

Horne believes that the relative importance of the three functions that are served by sleep – restoration, energy conservation, and a means of occupying time – will vary depending upon the species. Such factors as predation risk and cerebral development will be reflected in the value that is derived from sleep. Infants of various mammalian species show considerable brain development involving establishment of new neural systems, which might increase the need for core sleep (discussed later). Optional sleep might be favoured as a means of giving the parents some peace and quiet, and thereby opportunity to perform tasks such as foraging for food or sleeping themselves.

6.4.4 Sleep-deprivation studies

One possible means of getting some insight into the function served by sleep is to observe subjects who have volunteered to deprive themselves of it. In this regard, it is perhaps unfortunate that SK220 does not have a residential summer school, since these usually present an abundant supply of such volunteers, massively depriving themselves under the fairly 'natural conditions' of peer social pressure to do so. Most of them seem to perform remarkably well in tutorials and laboratory sessions over successive days, though we lack a rigorous study employing a matched control group who go to bed early after having completed a TMA.

One of the most notable sleep–deprivation subjects was Randy Gardner, a 17-year-old from California, who, in 1964, managed to go an incredible 264 hours without sleep, i.e. just short of 11 days. A team of friends was recruited with the task of working in shifts to keep him awake. Near to his home was a sleep laboratory, so he was able to get medical supervision and the researchers had a subject to study. Remarkably, there was no reason found for serious concern about any aspect of his health.

Certain changes in performance were noticed throughout the period. From day 2, he experienced difficulty in focusing his eyes and was unable to watch television from then on. At day 3, he started to experience changes in mood and some difficulties in speech. He experienced some nausea. From day 4, he became irritable and showed lapses of memory. His difficulty in concentration became clear to observers. Changes in visual perception were reported: he saw a fog around street lamps and experienced the illusion that a street sign took the form of a person. He imagined himself to be a great footballer and argued with those who would not believe him. From day 9, he reported a fragmentation of his thoughts and his sentences were incomplete. However, he maintained a grip on reality throughout and did not exhibit grossly disturbed ('psychotic') behaviour. Even towards the end of the deprivation period, his pulse, blood pressure and heart activity, as revealed by an electrocardiogram (ECG), were normal. Body temperature was about 11 °C below normal. Cerebral function, as indexed by eye movement control, memory and attention, was impaired.

Following this ordeal, Gardner went to bed but slept for only 14–15 hours, after which he awoke experiencing a complete reversal of the problems he had encountered during deprivation – for example, normal speech and memory returned. The REM periods observed during this first night of sleep were over three times the amount normally observed, suggestive of a compensation process.

Horne suggests that the key to Gardner's success in staying awake lay in his motivation to succeed, coupled with the support of his friends and having something interesting to occupy himself (e.g. walking around town and playing a pinball machine).

So what is the message from the Gardner study? Obviously, with just one subject, caution is in order. However, some pointers can be given and these correspond with the results for other sleep-deprived subjects. Only the brain appeared to show any adverse effects, the remainder of the body performing very well. However, as in other sleep-deprivation studies, there was no evidence of psychotic behaviour. A compensatory increase in REM sleep was evident in the sleep period following deprivation.

A sleep-deprivation study of 205 hours' duration carried out in 1966 on four subjects at the Neuropsychiatric Institute of the University of California at Los Angeles pointed to the same principal conclusion: that brain function is impaired but not to the extent of showing psychosis, with the remainder of the body able to cope very well.

6.4.5 A motivational perspective

One possible way of understanding sleep is to consider it in terms of motivation. You have already met the notion of motivation in Book 3, in the context of feeding and drinking. Motivation was said to arise from a complex of internal and external factors, such as nutrient levels, presence of food etc.

A particular motivation can have various strengths and there can be competing motivations. Sleep has some clear characteristics of motivation: when sleepy we are motivated to seek a suitable shelter. Sleep competes with other activities. When there is little else worth doing, the proportion of time spent sleeping increases. When waited upon hand and foot, domestic dogs and cats often seem to spend inordinate amounts of time sleeping. One supposes that, if left on their own, this time would be spent hunting. Similarly, consider how many people have to struggle hard to stay awake at conferences and lectures (but we hope that SK220 does not have a similar effect on you). The person may be bored with the lecture and unmotivated to listen attentively, and therefore another possible motivational candidate, that of sleep, usurps control.

The situation of wartime can bring extraordinary challenges for vigilance, and sleep can be missed. Making a task particularly interesting can prolong wakefulness. This suggests a kind of competition for control of behaviour.

So what does a motivational view have to say about the function served by sleep? Within limits, sleep shows flexibility, though that is not to deny a core component of sleep. Presumably reflecting the optional component, sleep can be shortened or extended according to prevailing circumstances. This would suggest that a system failure interpretation – for example, that neurons are unable to function any more without restoration – cannot account for all of sleep. On the basis of such a theory you might expect sleep to switch in regardless. The evidence suggests that sleep, or at least part of it, is a kind of optional activity which can be overridden if a more powerful motivation is present. However, there is a limit to flexibility and, after a time, sleep can overwhelm. In Horne's terms, optional sleep can only be stretched so far and then the dictates of core sleep are seen. Sadly, the experience of the Second World War suggests that a number of British pilots were killed by falling asleep in the cockpit.

6.4.6 Analogies

One way of trying to get insight into a complex system is to draw comparisons with other systems that we understand better. Such comparisons are termed **analogies**. The essence of an analogy is that we try to gain understanding of an unfamiliar system by seeing what it has in common with a system that is familiar and which we do understand. Analogies should only be pursued with caution since they might be misleading but persuasive all the same. However, the history of science shows that analogies have proven useful. One example is the comparison of biological regulatory systems with engineering equivalents.

In the case of the human brain, analogies are often drawn with computers. Both serve to process information by complex operations. So if the brain is something like a computer, is there anything in computer technology that resembles sleep?

Horne (1988) suggests the following as a possible analogy. In some computers 'spare circuits' are built into certain networks. If a failure occurs in one circuit, then automatic re-routing can occur through other circuits so as to bypass the problem. However, if such failures increase to a point where all the capacity has been used up, then a further circuit failure will become evident in a performance failure. By analogy with the brain, faults in neural circuits might be repaired during sleep and a failure of overall brain function will not occur for so long as there is a supply of spare circuits. This might last us up to about two nights of sleep loss but then the system becomes overwhelmed and failures of function (e.g. in processing information, memory) are seen. Up to this point, efforts of concentration by posing demanding tasks might be able to recruit more spare neural circuits. According to Horne's theory, by analogy with a computer, sleep represents a state of 'off-line', that is a state during which normal processing is switched off. Sleep is a necessary state for allowing repairs to occur, since normally in the waking state the brain will be permanently vigilant, engaged in directing one or other forms of behaviour and ready at any moment to switch behaviour in some other direction.

There are brain regions whose activity continues much the same throughout sleep and waking and which it would be unrealistic to expect to switch 'off-line'. The region of the lower part of the brain concerned with respiration is an example of this; presumably, it cannot switch off-line since the need for control of respiration is around-the-clock. The activity of such a region is largely pre-programmed and routine, unlike the cerebral cortex which is commonly exposed to novel situations. It might be for this reason that the cerebral cortex needs to switch off-line. It was the pioneer of sleep research, Guiseppi Moruzzi, who first pointed out that the lower brain region having a responsibility for the control of sleep, the reticular formation, paradoxically does not itself have a need to sleep (Horne, 1988, p. 143).

Summary of Section 6.4

1   The function served by sleep is not clear. There are a number of different theories that are not mutually exclusive; for example, (a) sleep is needed for a restorative function, (b) sleep serves the function of keeping us out of harm's way when we are at our most vulnerable, and (c) sleep serves to 're-program' the brain.

2   One proposal is for a distinction between core sleep and optional sleep.

3   The fact that all species studied exhibit sleep suggests that it serves some vital biological function.

4   In humans, studies suggest that brain function reversibly is impaired by sleep deprivation but the remainder of the body seems to function normally.

5   Sleep has the characteristics of a motivated activity.

6   Drawing an analogy between the brain and a computer network might give some insight into sleep. Each needs to go 'off-line' at times.

6.5 Developmental effects

In humans, the total amount of time spent in sleep in a night decreases from around 10 hours at age 6 to around 7 hours at age 30. It then increases to around 7.5 hours at age 70. Again, the longer periods of sleep in children correlate with, and could perhaps be explained in terms of, periods of brain development. It would seem reasonable to suggest that the young child is being bombarded with relatively large amounts of new information that needs to be assimilated. There is evidence that the circadian clock that normally governs sleep is functioning at birth (Ferber, 1994). However, it appears not to make connection with the control of sleep until an age of 6–12 weeks.

In humans, REM sleep appears to be at its greatest as a percentage of time in the fetus after 6 months of gestation (Horne, 1988; McCarley, 1994). Something like 15 hours of REM sleep can be shown in 24 hours. This could possibly be explained in terms of the high rate of brain development taking place at that stage. Large amounts of REM sleep appear to be necessary at this stage for central nervous system (CNS) development to occur. This observation suggests to some theorists that a general function of sleep throughout life is to serve some kind of restorative or restructuring role in terms of the CNS (Chokroverty, 1994).

A new-born human infant shows REM sleep for about one half of the total sleeping period. The figure is 67% in a baby born one month prematurely and 80% for one born two months prematurely. The new-born of other species, including most mammals and birds, show a similarly high percentage of REM sleep at around birth/hatching. However, there are exceptions to this generalization. These exceptions concern species born in a state described as *precocial*, meaning that they are born with their brains and physical abilities for movement already in a relatively advanced state.

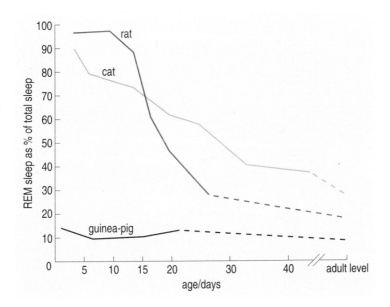

Figure 6.7   The percentage of total sleep time spent in REM sleep by three different species.

They are able to 'get up and go' rather quickly, as opposed to the relatively helpless human (by contrast, described as an *altricial* species). Examples of precocial species include the guinea pig, antelope and goat. Figure 6.7 compares a precocial species with two altricial species. Note the striking decline in percentage of REM sleep in the altricial species as a function of age.

The large percentage of REM sleep seen in new-born mammals of some species led a number of theorists to what is termed the **ontogenetic hypothesis** of REM sleep. This hypothesis suggests that REM sleep is closely connected with the development of the brain. With increasing age, the rate of development declines as does the percentage of REM sleep. In such terms, the percentage change of REM sleep over time following birth is so much less in a precocial species since development has largely preceded birth. According to the ontogenetic hypothesis, REM sleep is a way of providing the cerebral hemispheres with a particular pattern of stimulation necessary for neural development to occur. Following birth, such stimulation occurs via the sensory channels, but before birth, REM sleep provides a kind of substitute stimulation of the brain. In adulthood, REM sleep occurs at a certain relatively low level to provide some kind of stimulation needed to maintain the working efficiency of the brain. Efficient functioning might involve a regular process of undoing faulty connections between neurons and this could occur when the brain is off-line and during REM sleep.

Summary of Section 6.5

1   Human infants show a high percentage of REM sleep relative to adults.

2   Of all stages of life, the fetus at 6 months of gestation shows the highest percentage of REM sleep. This suggests that REM sleep might be serving a function in brain development.

3   The ontogenetic hypothesis of sleep suggests that REM sleep is connected with brain development.

6.6 Dreaming

If a subject is woken during the REM phase of sleep, he or she commonly (but not always) reports being in a dream. Dreams are also sometimes reported on awakening from non-REM sleep, though much less frequently. Sleep walking and the frightening phenomenon of night terrors (e.g. sudden screaming and thrusting of limbs) occur in SWS rather than the REM phase of sleep.

Dreams are mainly visual in their content and it appears that some dreamers do so in colour. How do blind people dream? People born blind or who have lost their sight while very young appear to dream mainly in the auditory modality and, to a lesser extent, the touch modality. People born blind do not show rapid eye movements during periods that otherwise (e.g. by the criterion of EEG recording) correspond to REM sleep. For those who suffer blindness later, there is evidence of rapid eye movements. It is perhaps difficult to imagine that the fetus would have much to dream about in spite of 15 hours of REM sleep per 24 hours.

Do non-human animals dream? Rapid eye movements are shown during sleep by most species of mammal. Some dog owners can confirm signs of agitation in their animals during sleep as if they are seeing off a rival. However, even for humans where the subject can be questioned, the study of mental states, e.g. dreams and consciousness, is difficult enough. The study in animals raises complex issues of scientific explanation.

Within the mainstream of neurobiology and psychology, there are various theories on the function of dreaming. Some theorists propose that dreaming serves no useful purpose but is simply a by-product of the brain's characteristic sleep-associated electrical activity. The bizarre nature of dreams with their sudden twists of story-line might simply represent the brain's attempts to impose some order upon an otherwise meaningless pattern of neural activity. Amongst other ideas is that dreaming represents a process of cataloguing the day's events. There might be a restructuring and reinterpretation of material acquired during the day, as manifest in dreams. This might involve removal of insignificant information. By analogy, libraries need to rearrange books in new categories, return borrowed books to their correct places on the shelves, occasionally throw out old unread volumes and accommodate new ones. It is not difficult to imagine that, in some cases, such work could be better carried out when the library is closed to visitors. Perhaps dreaming represents a process of throwing out unnecessary material from the brain's memory stores at a time when the brain is off-line. Times of trauma or stress might be ones at which negatively coloured material needs to be processed, which might 'throw up' the stuff of nightmares.

Outside the mainstream scientific tradition, a great deal has been written on the subject of the function of dreams. However, much of it is pure speculation.

Summary of Section 6.6

1   Dreams are a frequent occurrence in the REM phase of sleep.

2   One suggestion is that dreams correspond to a process of re-cataloguing the brain.

6.7 Issues of health and well-being

6.7.1 Introduction

Although no one is certain of why we need to sleep, disorders of sleep of various sorts constitute a major factor compromising the well-being of the population. For instance, in the USA, a report from the National Commission on Sleep Disorders Research in 1993 estimated that as many as 40 million Americans were troubled by chronic problems of disordered sleep and wakefulness (Edelman, 1994, p. ix). That includes one-third of all American adults. The majority of sufferers endure their problems untreated and even formally undiagnosed.

Throughout life there are changes in what constitutes the norm for sleep and against which disturbance can be compared. The sleep patterns of the fetus and new-born have already been described. Youth tends to show a clear circadian pattern divided into two periods of sleep and waking. Old age is commonly associated with a break-up of this pattern, consisting of frequent night-time waking and day-time naps. If this situation is exacerbated by degenerative disorders (e.g. dementia) it can amplify the problems of carers.

Some experts give a figure of 7 to 8 hours per 24 as the amount of sleep that the average adult requires. The figure is based upon studies showing that individuals who sleep less than 4 hours or more than 9 hours per night have an increased mortality from cancer, stroke or coronary artery disease compared to those sleeping between 7 and 8 hours. No differences in personality are evident comparing short and long sleepers. There are various epidemiological predictors of sleep disorders. These include old age, having a poor education and a low socio-economic status, having had a recent experience of stress, as well as drug and alcohol abuse (Chokroverty, 1994).

There is a variety of different disorders requiring various sorts of therapeutic intervention (e.g. insomnia, sleep walking, night terrors, excessive day-time sleepiness) but, because of time and space, this chapter can discuss only a few of these. One important technique is *chronotherapy* to shift a patient's circadian rhythm in order to make it correspond with the social norms of activity and inactivity. This is done using exposure to light at appropriate times in the cycle.

6.7.2 Insomnia

A common complaint seen by a general practitioner is that of **insomnia**, though the vast majority of sufferers (at least in the USA) appear not to seek medical help (Walsh, Hartman and Kowall, 1994). Insomnia is the most common of the sleep-related disorders and consists of a subjective feeling of an inadequacy of sleep.

A doctor hearing a complaint of insomnia should ideally look at the context of the whole person and the history of the condition. He or she should consider drug and alcohol consumption. Coffee drinking and cigarette smoking might be playing a role. Sometimes valuable insights can come from the patient's sleep partner (e.g. evidence of snoring, night terrors, or gasping for breath). The type of insomnia is important. For instance, early morning awakening is one of the symptoms of depression, so the patient's early waking hours might well be cruelly filled with black thoughts. In such a case, therapy for insomnia might logically be mediated through therapy for the depression.

Insomniacs commonly complain of poor work performance, irritability, fatigue and mood disturbances that they attribute to the insomnia. A higher frequency of automobile accidents is reported than for non-insomniacs. There is also some evidence to suggest that professional promotion prospects can suffer. Insomniacs have a higher frequency of other medical and psychological problems than do non-insomniacs. There is a higher mortality rate from various causes in insomniacs, compared to controls, including a higher frequency of heart attacks some six years after reports of poor sleep (Walsh, Hartman and Kowall, 1994).

Not surprisingly, teasing apart what is cause and what is effect is problematic. However, the evidence suggests that there can be a wide variety of different underlying causes of insomnia, including pain, shifts in the circadian rhythm as a result of irregular working hours, psychiatric disturbances and alcohol abuse. Insomnia can be a side-effect of medication for other conditions, e.g. beta-blockers (Chapter 5). Stress at the time of onset is reported by the majority of sufferers, and disruption of an important social bond is a very common causal factor. Insomnia is also a cause of itself; excessive worry about the condition tends to promote insomnia. However, in some cases, no cause can be identified.

The literature contains something of a contradiction concerning insomnia. Horne (1988) suggests that in fact loss of sleep *in itself* is not as harmful as is normally supposed, but not all experts would agree with this (Walsh, Hartman and Kowall, 1994). The nature of the problem created by insomnia might seem to run counter to Horne's argument that a large part of sleep can be described as optional (Section 6.4.2); why don't we just gladly accept as a bonus the time spared, to write better TMAs or OU courses or even to enjoy the occasional luxury of pursuing non-OU activities? Why is there an increased mortality from various causes amongst insomniacs if restitution of the body outside the central nervous system is not a function served by sleep? The answer is not clear. There might be some general biological function throughout the tissues of the body that is served by sleep and which we still don't know about. Another possibility is stress, that 'old faithful'. Insomnia is a highly stressful experience and it might be that this can account for subsequent ill-effects. If stress is the explanation, how might this arise?

Horne (1988, p. 208) suggests that we learn that we need a 'good eight hours' sleep a night' for our health, not to mention our beauty! This message is repeated endlessly in popular magazines. Since lack of sleep can be an index of illness (e.g. depression), a very common question posed by GPs is: 'How are you sleeping?' It is possible that the widespread assumption of the necessary eight hours' sleep can itself contribute to the anxiety that insomniacs experience. It is known that insomnia can fuel insomnia by the anxiety and frustration so aroused (Watts, East and Doyle, 1995). Insomniacs are rather bad at judging the length of time that it takes them to get to sleep, commonly overestimating by a factor of 3 (Walsh, Hartman and Kowall, 1994). Anxiety arising from a belief in the dangers of insomnia only serves to prolong the perceived passage of time.

The manufacturers of sleeping pills do little to dispel such anxiety, sleeping pills being one of the commonest prescriptions written. Experts are divided on their efficacy. Some argue for their use, particularly in the short term (Walsh, Hartman and Kowall, 1994). However, Horne (1988) argues that the benefits derived from sleeping pills, in terms of extra sleep, are very modest. Of course, the perceived benefits might be much bigger than the actual benefits in terms of sleep length, which could itself help to reduce anxiety and promote sleep. Most sleeping pills also reduce anxiety and so the perception of the gravity of insomnia can be reduced. Horne (1988, p. 208) makes the challenging statement:

> *I consider that physicians who unreservedly give out these prescriptions are unwittingly 'rewarding' the insomniac's beliefs about the seriousness of the condition.*

Coming off sleeping pills can be problematic and withdrawal effects are sometimes experienced. A gradual tapering of the dose over weeks can reduce the withdrawal effect.

6.7.3 Sleep hygiene

The term **sleep hygiene** refers to managing one's sleep, preferably without resort to pills. The advice is useful not just to chronic insomniacs but to all of us who wish to improve the quality of our sleep and who might occasionally have a bad night. The effects of applying sleep hygiene might not be so immediate as using sleeping pills and will require some working at but there are long-term sustainable benefits, without side-effects. The success rate is high.

Day-time naps tend to be more common in insomniacs compared to controls and, for young and middle-aged insomniacs, should be avoided. Naps are an inevitable part of the sleep profile of the elderly. Naps tend to reduce tiredness, the capacity to fall asleep at night-time and the strength of control over sleep exerted by the circadian rhythm. However, for good sleepers, naps can prove useful and do not necessarily impair night-time sleep.

Horne (1992) advises the insomniac to wake up at the same time each morning with the help of an alarm clock. This will help to maintain the control of the circadian rhythm. 'Sleep-ins' at the weekend are not allowed. The third point is that retiring to bed at night should only occur in response to sleepiness, not to the time indicated on the clock. If, on retiring, the subject fails to fall asleep, he or she should get up and perform some distracting but mundane activity until sleepiness is felt. This can be repeated on each occasion when sleep fails to ensue within 10 to 20 minutes. In this way, an association is formed between the bed and sleep not between the bed and the anxiety of insomnia. It would seem that sleep is no less susceptible to Pavlovian conditioning (Book 3, Chapter 6) than are the other behavioural phenomena discussed so far. It is therefore recommended that the bedroom not be used for regular non-sleeping activities (e.g. reading or watching television). Pavlovian conditioning can work in the sleeper's favour as well as against. Regular rocking of a child might acquire some its efficacy from its consistent pairing with sleep onset (Ferber, 1994).

There are various dietary and other recommendations, like taking care to avoid coffee, nicotine and alcohol, particularly near to sleep time. Caffeinated drinks should be limited to two cups per day, taken before noon. Sadly many insomniacs resort to alcohol as an aid, but this is not to be recommended. Vigorous activity near to bedtime, whether of a mental or physical kind, is to be discouraged. Physical exercise earlier in the day is encouraged. Light should be screened out of the bedroom.

For the elderly, although a certain amount of day-time napping might be inevitable, an extensive amount can subtract from night-time sleep. Such napping is often the natural result of boredom, which again emphasizes the value of maintaining interests in life that occupy the day-time hours. The elderly often feel sleepy at mid-evening and retire to bed. They then tend to awake at around 3 a.m. and are in fact alert and refreshed but tend not to construe such waking in positive terms. Rather they perceive that they are at a time when they should be asleep and worry about not getting back to sleep. Thus they might well spend up to 12 hours in sleep or an attempted sleep state. They might then resort to sleeping pills, the elimination of which from the body is relatively slow in the elderly, thereby increasing day-time sleepiness, a counter-productive effect. Horne recommends a mid-evening nap of about 20 minutes, using an alarm clock to prevent a full drift into night-time sleep. This can then enable the person to stay awake until around midnight and to sleep until around 5 a.m., a time that might be construed acceptably as early morning rather than as night.

6.7.4 Dreams

There is a popular view that we need to sleep in order to dream and that by dreaming we are discharging some kind of tension. Dream interpretation is something that attracts many, but the adventurer in this area should be warned of the hazards involved. It might well be that the overall quality of dreams, whether pleasant or nightmares, says something about a person's state of mental well-being. A high frequency of nightmares or night terrors might be indicative of stressful experiences in daily life. Recurrent nightmares not uncommonly follow trauma. However, there is no scientific evidence that the detailed contents of dreams can be interpreted for a hidden significance (e.g. the kind of idea popular in some circles that snakes and chimneys represent the male sex organ). Dream analyses by telephone or mail order should be treated with a special suspicion.

6.7.5 Sleep and accidents

Earlier we discussed two factors that contribute towards the tendency to sleep that would seem to be relevant to motor vehicle accidents: the time within the circadian rhythm and the interest value of the task being performed. It was noted that the tendency to sleepiness is highest at night and in the mid-afternoon. It was also noted that people undergoing sleep deprivation are able to resist sleep better by engaging in challenging tasks.

Motorway driving, as opposed to urban driving, is notorious for its monotony. Thus we might expect there to be an increased frequency of sleep-related accidents at certain points within the circadian rhythm. A report in the *British Medical Journal* looked at the evidence for this (Horne and Reyner, 1995). Of course, defining what is a sleep-related accident as opposed to any other presents certain problems. Drivers will not always admit to having fallen asleep at the wheel, and sadly in some cases they are no longer with us to tell what happened. However, working in collaboration with the police, Horne and Reyner devised some criteria for what they estimated were sleep-related accidents:

1   the subject was below the legal limit for alcohol consumption;

2   the vehicle ran off the road or into the back of another vehicle;

3   there were no signs of braking;

4   there were no mechanical defects evident in the vehicle;

5   the weather conditions were good and the visibility was good;

6   there was no evidence of speeding or prior driving too close to the vehicle in front;

7   the police attending the accident suspected sleep as the cause;

8   the setting of the accident was such that, for several seconds prior to it, the driver might have been expected to see the vehicle in front or the point of run off from the road.

With these stringent criteria that involved excluding even data that were 'strongly suggestive' but failed to meet all of the criteria, Horne and Reyner believed that, if anything, they erred on the side of underestimating sleep-related causes.

Devon and Cornwall constabulary provided data on accidents in the South West region of England over the period 1987–92. The data had been collected by the police before the investigation began and the police were not primed to look for sleep-related accidents. Sleep-related accidents comprised some 16–23% of total accident figures. Figure 6.8 shows the result of the survey. Three peaks can be clearly seen in the data, at 02.00–02.59, 06.00–06.59 and at 16.00–16.59. The other graph in Figure 6.8 shows traffic density over the 24-hour period.

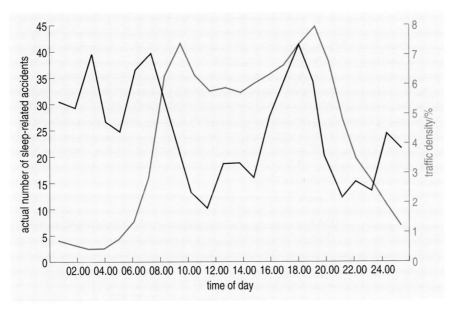

Figure 6.8   The frequency of sleep-related traffic accidents as a function of time over a 24-hour period. Also shown is the traffic density over the same period.

❑   Examine Figure 6.8. What is the reason for showing traffic density on the same graph? What is the conclusion to be drawn from it?

◼   If we are to interpret the accident peaks as representing a sleep-related effect it is necessary to rule out an explanation of the kind that these times simply correspond to peak traffic densities. It is clear that this is not the case. Density is very low at the time of the first two peaks and although it is high at the time of the third, it is also high at 10.00–10.59, which is the low point on the accident curve.

A report from the International Conference on Work Hours, Sleepiness and Accidents, held in Stockholm in 1994, highlighted the vital role of sleep in accidents and urged greater attention to working hours and rest breaks etc. (*Journal of Sleep Research*, 3, p. 195). It was concluded that sleepiness is under-reported as a factor in accidents. Of course, public knowledge can be empowering at a personal level. Motorists can choose to select times of journeys to avoid peak risk times. Journeys might sometimes be able to be broken for sleep pauses at such times.

Summary of Section 6.7

1 Insomnia is a common sleep disorder and corresponds to a subjective feeling of an inadequacy of sleep.

2 For reasons that are not entirely clear, insomnia tends to be associated with a number of bodily disorders and a relatively high vulnerability to accidents.

3 It is possible to try sleep hygiene techniques in order to bring sleep under control, e.g. to avoid naps and 'sleep-ins'.

6.8 Conclusions

After reading this chapter, you should have gained something of a feel for the present state of sleep research. Unlike the other behavioural phenomena discussed in SK220 (e.g. feeding, drinking and sexual behaviour), we still do not know the function of sleep for sure. However, we can make some intelligent speculation which maps onto an explanation in terms of the processes underlying sleep.

As in the other chapters, a holistic theme emerged in considering sleep. The chapter raised the possibility that sleep and insomnia can, to some extent, be influenced by our own knowledge of these processes, gained through cultural transmission. Thus our belief that sleep deprivation is very harmful might actually serve to exacerbate the effects of insomnia.

Sleep, rather than being simply a process of switching off behaviour, like a bedside table lamp is switched off, should be seen as a complex behaviour in its own right, involving conditioning. The final section on traffic accidents shows the vital importance of pursuing research into the biology and psychology of sleep. Other areas of research such as aircraft and industrial accidents could probably tell a similar story.

Objectives for Chapter 6

After reading this chapter you should be able to:

6.1 Define and use, or recognize definitions and applications of, each of the terms printed in **bold** in the text.

6.2 Describe the criteria for distinguishing different phases of sleep, e.g. (a) REM and non-REM sleep, and (b) core sleep and optional sleep. (*Question 6.1*)

6.3 Explain the criteria for a rhythm being described as 'circadian' and relate this to sleep and to the notion of zeitgeber. (*Question 6.2*)

6.4 Outline some of the approaches that researchers adopt in attempting to relate sleep to particular brain regions. (*Question 6.3*)

6.5 Describe some of the attempts that theorists have made to provide explanations for the function served by sleep and explain their implications for understanding the processes underlying sleep. (*Question 6.1*)

6.6 Relate sleep to development and thereby give a rationale for the ontogenetic hypothesis. (*Question 6.4*)

6.7 Relate observations on the effect of sleep disturbances to theories on the bases of sleep. (*Question 6.5*)

6.8 Make recommendations to improve the quality of a person's sleep and efficiency during waking hours. (*Question 6.5*)

Questions for Chapter 6

Question 6.1 (*Objectives 6.2 and 6.5*)

Suppose we make dramatic progress in the neurobiology of sleep and, by an insightful analysis of the nervous system of a certain species of animal, we were able to establish that it needs only 2 hours of core sleep in 24 hours. (a) What exactly might be meant by such a statement? (b) In its natural habitat the species is observed to sleep for 10 hours. Would this mean that 8 hours of sleep serves no function?

Question 6.2 (*Objective 6.3*)

The blood level of a certain chemical is measured in some human subjects and it is shown to cycle up and down with a period of 24 hours. Is that observation sufficient to enable you to conclude that a circadian rhythm is involved?

Question 6.3 (*Objective 6.4*)

Cocaine is described as a dopamine reuptake inhibitor (Book 2, Chapter 3). For users of this substance, (a) cocaine increases wakefulness and (b) abstinence from cocaine and similar substances is associated with sleep. What does this suggest about the role of dopaminergic neurons in the brain?

Question 6.4 (*Objective 6.6*)

Does the ontogenetic hypothesis of sleep conflict with other explanations of sleep such as that sleep serves a restorative function or that it serves to keep us out of harm's way when we are most vulnerable?

Question 6.5 (*Objectives 6.7 and 6.8*)

Explain some of the ways in which an holistic approach to sleep, calling upon information from various levels of understanding, is likely to be more useful than seeking information at only the one level.

References

Chokroverty, S. (1994) *Sleep Disorders Medicine: Basic Science, Technical Considerations and Clinical Aspects*, Butterworth-Heinemann, Boston, MA.

Edelman, N. H. (1994) Foreword, in *Sleep Disorders Medicine: Basic Science, Technical Considerations and Clinical Aspects* (ed. S. Chokroverty), Butterworth-Heinemann, Boston, MA, p. ix.

Ferber, R. (1994) Sleep disorders of childhood, in *Sleep Disorders Medicine: Basic Science, Technical Considerations and Clinical Aspects* (ed. S. Chokroverty), Butterworth-Heinemann, Boston, pp. 417–428.

Guyton, A. C. (1991) *Textbook of Medical Physiology*, W. B. Saunders, Philadelphia.

Horne, J. (1988) *Why We Sleep*, Oxford University Press, Oxford.

Horne, J. (1992) Insomnia, *The Psychologist* (May), pp. 216–218.

Horne, J. A. and Reyner, L. A. (1995) Sleep related vehicle accidents, *British Medical Journal*, **310**, 565–567.

de Jesus Cabeza, R., Zoltoski, R. K. and Gillin, J. C. (1994) Biochemical pharmacology of sleep, in *Sleep Disorders Medicine: Basic Science, Technical Considerations and Clinical Aspects* (ed. S. Chokroverty), Butterworth-Heinemann, Boston, MA, pp. 37–56.

McCarley, R. W. (1994) Neurophysiology of sleep: basic mechanisms underlying control of wakefulness and sleep. In *Sleep Disorders Medicine: Basic Science, Technical Considerations and Clinical Aspects* (ed. S. Chokroverty), Butterworth-Heinemann, Boston, MA, pp. 17–36.

Meddis, R. (1977) *The Sleep Instinct*, Routledge and Kegan Paul, London.

Walsh, J. K., Hartman, P. G. and Kowall, J. P. (1994) Insomnia, in *Sleep Disorders Medicine: Basic Science, Technical Considerations and Clinical Aspects* (ed. S. Chokroverty), Butterworth-Heinemann, Boston, MA, pp. 219–239.

Watts, F. N., East, M. P. and Coyle, K. (1995) Insomniacs' perceived lack of control over sleep, *Psychology and Health*, **10**, 81–95.

ANSWERS TO QUESTIONS

Chapter 2

Question 2.1

The X and Y chromosomes behave as a pair during meiosis because they contain many homologous sequences. The Y chromosome is believed to have evolved from the X chromosome, with some additions from autosomes. The regions of the Y that pair with the X are essential to prevent the Y from being lost.

Question 2.2

Your answer could include any four of the following: growth of body hair; enlargement of the genitals and change in body shape to a more adult form (both sexes); enlargement of the larynx leading to the voice breaking and growth of facial hair (males); development of the breasts (females). All these features, signalling as they do a change in reproductive status, are likely to affect a person's emotions. However, the features most likely to cause embarrassment are voice breaking and breast growth.

Question 2.3

(a) The most important hormonal influence on the development of the genitals is the effect of testosterone which, if present during a critical time period, alters development from the female pathway to the male pathway. Also, the testis Sertoli cells produce anti-Müllerian hormone which causes regression of the Müllerian ducts, thereby preventing growth of the female organs.

(b) The mammary glands develop the ability to secrete milk under the influence of oestrogen, progestogen, prolactin and possibly placental lactogen.

Question 2.4

The sexual urge is very strong, and if people were to satisfy their desire for intercourse indiscriminately, there would be unwanted relationships and unwanted babies. Furthermore, most societies have rules relating to wealth and status, and would not wish these to be broken by sexual activities. So rules of sexual etiquette have developed to allow channelling of sexual activity into approved routes which do not interfere with the *status quo*.

Question 2.5

Sex hormones are thought to influence behaviour, but do not determine it in humans: many other factors affect how human beings behave in a given situation. For example, testosterone is believed to influence sex drive, but the level of testosterone in the blood is not a predictor of whether or not intercourse will take place.

Question 2.6

First, a woman must decide if she needs analgesia during labour – many do not. Second, she must consider what form the pain relief should take, bearing in mind what is available. She might also consider whether she wants control of the administration of analgesia, such as is possible with TENS or inhalation of gas and air, or whether she would prefer a total pain block, such as occurs with an epidural. Finally, but importantly, she must bear in mind that any drug is likely to affect her baby as well as herself.

Question 2.7

Common symptoms mentioned in the text are: cessation of menstrual periods (caused by loss of sensitivity of the follicles to pituitary hormones), hot flushes (caused by a lowering of the body's temperature set-point), dry skin (caused by low oestrogen levels which allow collagen to disintegrate), itchiness (caused by degenerating nerve endings in the skin), dry vagina (caused by low oestrogen levels which affect the epithelium), osteoporosis (caused by an oestrogen-sensitive change in the balance of bone synthesis and degradation), and emotional effects, for which there is no reductionist explanation.

Chapter 3

Question 3.1

Normally the term 'circle of sexual arousal' refers to the fact that central motivation excites a genital response, which then contributes to strengthen the central motivation, and so on. An erectile failure, for example, would of course mean that the usual feedback from aroused genitals does not occur. In this sense, the circle is broken. However, perhaps the term 'vicious circle' is more appropriate. Thus erectile failure can have negative effects upon central arousal and induce performance anxiety. This can serve to exacerbate the local dysfunction, which then feeds back to the brain, a classic vicious circle.

Question 3.2

Vasoconstriction of the small arteries supplying blood to the genitals.

Question 3.3

A high level of activity in both neurons 1 and 5 and no activity in neuron 6.

Question 3.4

Hormones and their effects in sensitizing the nervous system processes underlying motivation and behaviour are a feature that we share with many other animal species. Hormones have effects on the nervous system such that stimuli in the environment arouse sexual desire in us. The hormones involved are not peculiar to humans. However, humans possess a rich imagination, unlike non-humans. Also the developmental path to adult sexuality is dependent upon a set of peculiarly human cultural influences which encourage some behaviours and condemn others. Language in the form of conversations with others and through print and audiovisual media will present certain images and possibilities for the development of sexual motivation.

Question 3.5

A hormone is a chemical released at one site in the body, which is transported in the bloodstream and effects an action at some distant location. In the present context, one of the principal hormones under consideration is testosterone. In men this is released from the testes and exerts effects upon the brain. During the critical period it plays a part in *organizing* certain neural structures such that they later have a potential for arousing sexual motivation and behaviour. An *activational* effect refers to a later effect of the hormone in arousing motivation.

Question 3.6

An antagonist is a substance that occupies receptor sites that are normally occupied by a natural transmitter and which blocks the action of the transmitter. In the context of Figure 3.4, an antagonist to the transmitter employed at either of the excitatory synapses would lower sexual motivation. An antagonist to the inhibitory neurotransmitter would increase sexual motivation, as described in Section 3.3.2.

Chapter 4

Question 4.1

Logically pain (unlike light or sound) is not something out there in the environment to be detected. Rather it is an inner emotional experience. Also nociceptor activity and pain do not always closely correspond. There can be tissue damage (and nociceptor activation) with little pain experienced and conversely a pain experience but without tissue damage and nociceptor activity (e.g. a phantom limb experience 'in' a missing limb).

Question 4.2

By rubbing the eyes presumably activity is set up in large-diameter fibres. It would seem that this serves to inhibit the effects of the nociceptors that are active in this condition. It suggests that something comparable to the gate that is in the spinal cord is also present in the pathways that convey tactile information in the cranial nerves of the head.

Question 4.3

Lignocaine is something locally applied to a particular site of peripheral tissue damage, e.g. the mouth at the time of dental surgery. It affects all neurons, whether afferent (carrying noxious or innocuous information) or efferent. Since the tissue damage arises at the heart it would be necessary to target neurons conveying information from the heart. It is difficult, if not impossible, to see how this could be done in practice since afferent and efferent fibres are close together (see Book 2, Chapter 3) and it would risk disturbing the control of the heart's activity.

Question 4.4

1 a; 2 b. With reference to Figure 4.4 (and 4.3c), an agonist to substance P released from the nociceptive neuron increases excitation of the T cell, resulting in the experience of pain; an enkephalin agonist increases the inhibition from neuron S, thereby reducing activity in the T cell and so exerting an analgesic effect.

Question 4.5

In the phantom limb, connections between peripheral neurons and the central nervous system are broken. Nonetheless, both the noxious and innocuous sensations reported in a phantom limb refer to experiences that normally arise as a result of both of these types of afferent stimulation. In some cases, these sensations were earlier experienced as a result of sensory stimulation in the intact limb in question. For example, a ring that was tight on a finger is still felt as tight even after loss of the arm.

Question 4.6

Consider first the extent to which Pavlovian conditioning played a role in the development of the placebo effect and its similarity to salivary conditioning. If it works along similar lines then repeated presentation of the placebo without any pharmacologically active associated procedure might be expected to diminish its impact. As far as a belief in its efficacy is concerned, then a loss of faith in the carer and of belief in the treatment's efficacy might be sufficient to diminish the actual efficacy of a placebo.

Question 4.7

A response 'no stronger than when using a placebo' would mean that some substance without any of the specificity of the new drug would achieve as strong an analgesic effect. In order to test the claim rigorously, a double-blind study (Section 4.8.1) would have to be carried out.

Chapter 5

Question 5.1

Your response might be something like as follows. We are social creatures who have evolved in a world in which social bonds have been vital for our survival. We believe that our psychological world of thoughts and emotions is organized in the brain, as is social bonding. We know that there are links between those brain processes responsible for emotions and the endocrine system. We know that events in the nervous and endocrine system affect the state of both the circulatory and the immune systems.

Question 5.2

The term is a summary of a sequence of causal links. The sequence of events starts at the hypothalamus, part of the central nervous system. Neurons originating in the hypothalamus secrete corticotropin-releasing hormone (CRH) which is transported to the pituitary gland. This gland represents the interface between the nervous and endocrine systems. At the pituitary gland, CRH triggers the release of adrenocorticotropic hormone (ACTH). This is transported via the bloodstream to the adrenal glands where it stimulates the release of corticosteroids from the cortex. Levels of corticosteroids are controlled by their negative feedback effect on CRH and ACTH secretion from the hypothalamus and pituitary gland respectively (Figure 5.2).

Question 5.3

Most hormones are released into the bloodstream and influence one or more targets some distance away. CRH is atypical in that it is released into a particular *local* blood vessel in which it is transported to its single nearby target, without entering the general circulation.

Question 5.4

A well-controlled study might put the subject in a stress-evoking situation prior to therapy and measure the responses of the sympathetic nervous system (e.g. adrenalin level) and of the corticosteroid system. Following therapy, these measurements would be repeated. If the therapy were successful then a diminution in the responsiveness of these two systems might be expected.

Question 5.5

The rats would be injected with a chemical (unconditional stimulus) that has an immunosuppressive effect (unconditional response). This procedure would be carried out in the presence of a stimulus (e.g. odour) that has no capacity to produce immunosuppression (neutral stimulus). Following a few pairings of the odour and the injection, the capacity of the odour (conditional stimulus) to evoke immunosuppression would be measured (conditional response). (A control group would also need to be employed as a comparison.)

Chapter 6

Question 6.1

(a) Such a claim would probably mean that we had identified some kind of vital neural repair function that occurs at times of sleep. This repair is complete by 2 hours of sleep.

(b) It would be unlikely that such a long sleep would have evolved if it served no function. It is more likely that the animal is relatively ineffective if active during these 8 hours (e.g. vulnerable to predation, unable to see in the dark) and therefore the function is one of 'enforced' inactivity.

Question 6.2

No. You would also need to esablish that there is an intrinsic generation of the rhythm. You would need to put the subject in isolation from their normal daily routine and from the 24-hour day/night cycle and see whether the same rhythm continues.

Question 6.3

By blocking dopamine reuptake, the level of dopamine at dopaminergic synapses is increased. This tends to increase the activity of the postsynaptic neuron at such synapses. The fact that this is associated with increased wakefulness suggests that activity in dopaminergic neurons might normally play a role in maintaining wakefulness. This suggestion is supported by the observation that abstinence from cocaine (or other dopamine reuptake inhibitors) can be associated with sleep, for in the absence of the reuptake inhibitor dopamine level at the synapse would be expected to decrease. This would lower the efficacy of the synapse and hence lower the level of postsynaptic activity.

Question 6.4

No. First, the hypothesis refers only to REM sleep. Second, we might expect that sleep would serve various functions. For something to persist throughout life strongly suggests that it has a function during all stages of life.

Question 6.5

Clearly we need information at the biological level, looking at individual neurotransmitters and brain regions. Disturbed sleep might correspond to disturbed neurotransmitter levels, as described for certain drug users. However, if we *only* consider evidence at this level then we are likely to miss important sources of insight. Thus even though disturbed sleep might well correspond to disturbances in neurotransmitter levels within the central nervous system, this does not mean that the CNS is the only possible site of intervention. Adopting such a reductionist approach would lead simply to the solution of taking sleeping pills. As we have seen, there are behavioural interventions that can be tried to counter insomnia. Also the information transmitted in our culture might actually influence our sleep. The widespread notion that we need 8 hours of sleep a night might help to lead to stress as a result of insomnia, a kind of self-fulfilling prophecy.

ACKNOWLEDGEMENTS

We are grateful to Jean Macqueen who prepared the index for this book.

Grateful acknowledgement is made to the following sources for permission to reproduce material in this book:

Covers

Front and *back*: Copyright © 1995 Comstock Inc.

Figures

Figure 2.5: Tanner, J. M. (1980) *Growth at Adolescence*, Blackwell Science Ltd; *Figure 2.6:* Frisch, R. E. (1972) *Pediatrics*, **50**, pp. 445–450, American Academy of Pediatrics; *Figures 2.8 and 2.10:* Johnson, M. and Everitt, B. (1980) *Essential Reproduction*, 4th edn, Blackwell Science Ltd, by permission of authors and publisher; *Figure 2.11(i):* Odent, M. 'Genèse de l'homme écologique' (Épi, 1979); *Figure 2.11(ii):* Engelmann, G. J. 'Labor among primitive peoples' (St Louis, J. H. Chambers, 1882) p.13; *Figure 2.11(iii):* Courtesy of Sally and Richard Greenhill; *Figure 2.11(iv):* Childbirth scene by Joost Amman, from Jacob Rueff's De generatione hominis (1580), reproduced from *Medicine and the Artist* (Ars Medica) by permission of Philadelphia Museum of Art; *Figure 2.14:* Stoppard, M. (1986) *Pregnancy and Birth Handbook*, Dorling Kindersley; *Figure 2.17:* Mepham, T. B. (1987) *Physiology of Lactation*, Open University Press, by permission of the author; *Figures 3.3 and 6.1:* Guyton, A. C. (1991) *Textbook of Medical Physiology*, W. B. Saunders & Co., Inc.; *Figure 3.5:* Bancroft, J. (1989) *Human Sexuality and its Problems*, Churchill Livingstone; *Figure 5.4:* Williams, R. (1989) *The Trusting Heart*, Times Books, Inc.; *Figure 6.7:* Jouvet-Mounier, D., Astic, L. and Lacote, D. (1968) 'Ontogenesis of the states of sleep in the rat, cat and guinea pig during the first post-natal month', *Developmental Psychobiology*, **2**, pp. 216–239, reproduced by permission of John Wiley and Sons, Inc.; *Figure 6.8:* Horne, J. A. and Reyner, L. A. (1995) 'Sleep-related vehicle accidents', *British Medical Journal*, **310**, 4 March 1995, British Medical Journal Publishing Group.

INDEX

Note: Entries in **bold** are key terms. Page numbers in *italics* refer to figures and tables.